IN   948964-21-9 1

G000036646

0262-9712

from 1760 in rising order of face-value
QUARTER-FARTHINGS to CROWNS
DECIMAL CENT to FIVE POUNDS

Copper, Bronze, Silver, Nickel-brass and Cupro-nickel

EVERY non-gold coin from 1760 separately listed for:

GEORGE III   House of HANOVER 1760 - 1820
GEORGE IV   House of HANOVER 1820 - 1830
WILLIAM IV   House of HANOVER 1830 - 1837
VICTORIA   House of HANOVER 1837 - 1901
EDWARD VII   SAXE-COBURG   1901 - 1910
GEORGE V   House of WINDSOR 1910 - 1936
EDWARD VIII   House of WINDSOR   1936
GEORGE VI   House of WINDSOR 1936 - 1952
ELIZABETH II   House of WINDSOR 1952 to date

Over TWO HUNDRED YEARS and NINE REIGNS

Photographs of coins, and information extracted from its reports,
are reproduced with the permission of the Royal Mint.

A compilation of averaged selling-prices drawn from
dealers' lists, auctions and numismatic magazines by

R. J. Marles for:

ROTOGRAPHIC PUBLICATIONS - 37 St. Efrides Road
Torquay - TQ2 5SG - ENGLAND

QUARTER FARTHINGS FOR USE IN CEYLON

Date	Mintage		Fine	V.F.	E.F.	abt Unc/FDC
VICTORIA						COPPER
1839	3,840,000		£2	£9	£25	£40/£60
1851			£3	£12	£30	£45/£75
1852	2,215,000		£2	£9	£18	£35/£55
1853			£4	£12	£24	£50/£75
1853	Proofs		(from the sets)		---	£200
1853	Cupro-nickel proofs		(P1615)		---	£260
1868	Bronze proofs		(P1616)		---	£200

THIRD FARTHINGS FOR USE IN MALTA

GEORGE IV						COPPER
1827			£2	£4	£15	£40/£55
1827	Proof		---	--	£45	£175/£200
WILLIAM IV						COPPER
1835			£2	£4	£16	£40/£65
1835	noted (Seaby 1990)		GEF much lustre £25			---/---
1835	Proof		---	---	£160	---/---
VICTORIA						
1844	1,301,040 COPPER		£3	£10	£30	£45/£60
noted	(P1606)		(Seaby 1989 GEF £60)			---
1844	RE (for REG)		(P1607)	---	£225	£300/£400
1844	Large 'G'		---	£10	£30	£45/£60
1866	576,000 BRONZE		50p	£2	£6	£14/£20
1868	144,000 "		40p	£2	£8	£20/£30
1876	162,000 "		60p	£2	£6	£18/£25
1878	288,000 "		40p	£2	£6	£16/£20
1881	144,000 "		60p	£2	£7	£15/£18
1884	144,000 "		50p	£2	£4	£12/£16
1885	288,000 "		45p	£2	£4	£10/£16
	Proofs: 1866 £135; 1868, 1876, 1881 rarely seen.					
EDWARD VII						BRONZE
1902	288,000		---	£1	£2	£4/£6
1902	noted (Seaby 1990)		---	---	abt Unc £6	
GEORGE V						BRONZE
1913	288,000		---	£1	£2.50	£5/£8

HALF FARTHINGS FOR USE IN CEYLON

GEORGE IV						COPPER
1828	7,680,000 Rev A		£3	£7	£30	£75/£95
1828	Noted (Seaby 1990)		E.F. + lustre £60			---/---
1828	Rev B see below		£10	£30	£75	£150/£250
1830	8,776,320		£2	£8	£30	£80/£100
1830	Smaller date		£3	£16	£60	---/----
1830	Rev B see below		£12	£40	£85	£175/----

A number of proofs occur but no transactions noted.
Rev A: trident reaches above base of letters
Rev B: the trident reaches base of letters

Date	Mintage		Fine	V.F.	E.F.	Unc/abt. FDC.
WILLIAM IV						COPPER
1837	1,935,360		£10	£32	£100	£150/£180
1837	Noted		(Seaby 1990) GVF £45			—/—
VICTORIA			COPPER EXCEPT WHERE INDICATED			
1839	2,042,880		---	£3	£10	£25/£40
1842			---	£2	£9	£22/£36
1842	Noted (Traynor 1990)		UNC with lustre			£14/---
1843	3,440,640		---	£1	£4	£8/£16
1844	6,451,000		---	£1	£2	£4/£8
1844	E of REGINA over N		£3	£12	£30	£40/---
1847	3,010,560		---	£3	£9	£18/£30
1851	Unknown	P1597	£2	£5	£15	£30/£45
1851	1 struck over 5		---	£15	---	---
1852	989,184		---	£5	£18	£30/£45
1853	955,224		£1	£6	£25	£40/£65
1854	677,376		£1	£7	£26	£42/---
1856	913,920	P1603	£1	£8	£30	£40/£65
1856	Large date		£16	£36	(not in Peck)	
1868	Bronze proof	P1605	---	---	---	---/£175
1868	Cupro-nickel proof		---	---	---	---/£200

Proofs 1839 £200; 1853 £250; 1853 bronze £200

Date	Mintage	Peck No.	Fine	V.F.	E.F.	abt Unc/FDC

GEORGE III   LONDON MINT - DATE BELOW BRITANNIA

Date	Mintage	Peck No.	Fine	V.F.	E.F.	abt Unc/FDC
1771		P909	£8	£25	£60	£125/£250
1771	Proof	P910	- - -	- - -	- - -	- - -/£500
1773		P911	£1	£5	£30	£60/£95
1773	No stop Rev.	P912	£6	£16	£50	£100/- - -
1773	Obverse 2	P913	£2	£10	£30	- - -
1773	Obverse 2	P914	No stop Rev.	£20		£80/- - -
1773	No stop after Rex		£8	£25		on Peck 914
1774	Obverse 1	P915	£2	£9	£30	£60/£85
1774	Obverse 2	P916	£14	noted (1991)		
1775		P917	£3	£12	£40	£95/£140
1775	Inverted A for V	V in GEORGIVS		£65		- - -/- - -
1790	Pattern in silver	P1034	- - -	- - -		£650
1790	Pattern in copper	P1035	- - -	- - -	- - -	£450

SOHO (Birmingham) MINT - DATE BELOW BUST

Date	Mintage	Peck No.	Fine	V.F.	E.F.	abt Unc/FDC
1797	Pattern	P1199	- - -	- - -	- - -	£295
1797	Pattern	P1201	- - -	- - -	- - -	£225
1797	Pattern	P1202	- - -	- - -	- - -	£225
1798	Pattern	P1203	- - -	£95	- - -	£250
1798	Pattern	P1204	- - -	- - -	- - -	£220
1798	Pattern	P1212	- - -	- - -	- - -	£200
1798	Pattern	P1215	- - -	- - -	- - -	£280
1799	Three berries	P1279	£1	£3	£15	£25/£60
1799	Four berries	P1280	- - -	- - -	£70	£200/£350
1799	Proofs and Patterns abound,		averaging			£90/£260
1799	Proof	P1390	bronzed	noted	FDC	£90
1799	Proof but with groove as currency		GEF	£45		- - -
1805	Pattern	P1319	bronzed	noted	FDC	£275
1806	Portrait 1	P1396	- - -	£2	£10	£22/£40
1806	Portrait 2	P1397	£1	£3	£12	£30/£50
1806	Incuse dot	P1398	- - -	£20	£40	£80/£125
1807	Portrait 1	P1399	£3	£7	£15	£45/£85

Obverse 1 has row of breastplate scales, broken by rose at centre
Obverse 2 has a full, unbroken, row of eight scales

GEORGE IV   Laureate Head   DATE BELOW BRITANNIA

Date	Mintage	Peck No.	Fine	V.F.	E.F.	abt Unc/FDC
1821	2,688,000	P1407	£1	£3	£12	£20/£45
1821	G of GRATIA over O	(Colin Cooke mint state £69)				
1821	Proof in copper		- - -	- - -	- - -	£350/- - -
1822	5,924,352	P1409	50p	£2	£10	£20/£45
1822	Proof in copper		- - -	- - -	- - -	£350/- - -
1822	Obverse 2	P1411	50p	£2	£10	£40/£50
1823	2,365,440	P1412	£1	£3	£12	£25/£45
1823	Date has I for 1		£5	£16	£30	£60/£95

All dies are punched more than once. If one blow fails to register with another, then figures appear doubled, even trebled: this is very common. A major misalignment, however, will add value to the coin.
Obverse 1: Peck says 'the leaf-midribs (if present) are single raised lines'
Obverse 2: The 3 lowest leaves have incuse midribs.

FARTHINGS

Date	Mintage	Peck No.	Fine	V.F.	E.F.	Unc/abt FDC
GEORGE IV Laureate Head (continued) DATE BELOW BRITANNIA						
1825	4,300,800	P1414	---	£2	£12	£35/£50
1825	5 over 3 - a recent "find" offered @ £25 (Fine only) ---					
1825	D of DEI over U		£10	£40	£90	---
1825	Obverse 2	P1414A	£2	£6	£16	£28/£45
1825	Proof in gold	P1415	---	---	extremely rare	
1826	6,666,240	P1416	£1	£3	£15	£35/£50
1826	I for 1	noted	£80	---	---	£350/---
Undraped or Bare Head DATE BELOW HEAD						
1826	Inc. above	P1439	£1	£3	£12	£45/£60
1826	Bronzed Proof	P1440	---	---	£50	£100/£150
1826	Copper Proof	P1441	---	---	£60	---
1827	2,365,440	P1442	£1	£4	£18	£40/£65
1828	2,365,440	P1443	£1	£3	£12	£35/£60
1829	1,505,280	P1444	£2	£8	£20	£50/£75
1830	2,365,440	P1445	---	£2	£15	£40/£55

1825 seems to have been a 'bad' year for the die-makers:
re-strikes/re-cuts of dies both obverse and reverse   along
with flaws at neck and trident.

Date	Mintage	Peck No.	Fine	V.F.	E.F.	abt. Unc/FDC
WILLIAM IV			DATE BELOW HEAD - 21mm			
1831	2,688,000	P1466	£1	£3	£20	£45/£65
1831	Proof	P1467	----	bronzed		£200/£300
1831	Proof	P1468	inverted reverse			---/£150
1831	Proof	P1469	----	copper		---/£375
1834	1,935,360	P1470	£1	£3	£20	£50/£70
1834	Reverse B	P1471	£2	£5	£25	£60/£85
1835	1,720,320	P1472	£2	£7	(reverse A)	
1835	Reverse B	P1473	£1	£4	£15	£40/£65
1836	1,290,240	P1474	£1	£5	£18	£50/£75
1837	3,010,560	P1475	£1	£3	£12	£45/£70

Reverse B has raised line down the arms of saltire
(cross of St.Andrew); whereas A has incuse line

VICTORIA Young Head

Date	Mintage	Peck No.	Fine	V.F.	E.F.	abt. Unc/FDC
			DATE BELOW HEAD - 21mm			
1838	591,360	P1553	£1.25	£3	£10	£30/£45
1838	DEF : on	P1553	£3	£6	£25	---/---
1839	4,300,800	P1554	£1	£3	£9	£20/£40
1839	Proofs in copper, some bronzed. Bronzed					---/£180
1839	Two pronged trident		---	£3	£9	£20/£65
1840	3,010,560	P1559	£1	£3	£12	£20/£40
1840	Variety on	P1559	DEF.	£3	£12	---/---
1841	1,720,320	P1560	£1	£3	£13	£18/£30
1841	Varieties P1560	REG.	and		REG for REG	£20/£30
1841	Proof	P1561	If offered could fetch £800			
1842	1,290,240	P1562	£3	£7	£20	£45/---
1842	Variety on P1562		£5 large '42' in date			
1843	Struck over 1842		---	---	---	---/---
1843	4,085,760	P1563	£1	£3	£10	£20/£50
1843	I for 1 in date		£25	£50	£100	£200/---
1844	430,080	P1565	£15	£40	(1991)	£550
1845	3,225,600	P1566	£1	£3	£12	£25/£60
1845	Large date	F/GF	£45	(Colin Cooke 1991)		
1846	2,580,480	P1567	£2	£8	£32	£60/---
1847	3,879,720	P1568	£1	£3	£10	£20/£50
1847	Proof		You could get £1100 for yours!			
1848	1,290,246	P1569	£1	£4	£12	£25/£60
1849	645,120	P1570	£6	£21	£50	£200
1850	430,080	P1571	£1	£4	£14	£28/£42
1850	5 over inverted 5	9	---	---		---/---
	possibly, 5 over damaged 5 (no upright stroke) and much like a 3					
1850	5 over 4	(1991)	nEF	£25	abtUNC £45	
1851	1,935,360	P1572	£6	£15	£30	£60/£95
1851	D of DEI STRUCK OVER ꓷ		£200	£500	---	---/---
1852	822,528	P1574	£5	£15	£30	£80/£120

HARINGTON and LENNOX farthing tokens are to be found in
"Collectors' Coins: Ireland" (they feature the 'Irish' harp).
From James I to Charles I there were Richmond rounds - Transitional
Maltravers rounds, Richmond ovals and Maltravers ovals. These too are
to be found in "COLLECTORS COINS: IRELAND".

Date	Mintage	Peck No.	Fine	V.F.	E.F.	Unc/abt. FDC

VICTORIA Young Head   DATE BELOW HEAD

Date	Mintage	Peck No.	Fine	V.F.	E.F.	Unc/abt. FDC
1853	1,028,628	P1575	30p	£1	£4	£16/£25
1853	3 struck over 2	- -	- -	- - -	- - -	£45/£70
1853	Proof, bronzed, with inverted reverse		- - -	- - -	- - -	- - -/- - -
1853	Proof with raised W.W. P1577			- - -	- - -	£250/£350
1853	WW incuse	P1578	£2	£6	£15	£25/£40
1853	Proof with incuse W W P1579			- - -	- - -	£200/£300
1854	6,504,960	P1580	£1	£3.50	£10	£25/£50
1855	3,440,640	P1581	W W	incuse	£20	£45/£90
1855	Included	P1582	W.W.	raised	£20	£45/£90
1856	1,771,392	P1583	£3	£6	£20	£45/£90
★1856	R over E (VICTORIA) P1584		£60	£100	£325/- - -
1857	1,075,200	P1585	£1	£2.50	£10	£20/£40
1858	1,720,320	P1586	£1	£3	£8	£20/£35
1858	Small date		£10	£20	£40	- - -/- - -
1859	1,290,240	P1587	£5	£15	£50	£75/£125
1860	Obverse date currency		C. Cooke 1990 abt Unc £3900
1860	Obverse date proof		C. Cooke 1990 abt Unc £3600
1864		P1589 Colin Cooke not selling even at £7,500!

VICTORIA "Bun" Head

BRONZE - DATE BELOW BRITANNIA - 20mm
BB = Border of Beads   TB = Toothed Border

Date	Mintage	Peck No.	Fine	V.F.	E.F.	Unc/abt. FDC
1860	2,867,200 with various "Berries-in-Wreath" obverses:
1860	BB 3 berries	P1854	£1.50	£4	£10	£18/£27
1860	Proof	P1856	- - -	- - -	- - -	£175
1860	MULE combining beaded and toothed borders:
		P1857	£100	£150	£250	- - -/- - -
1860	TB 4 berries	P1858	20p	£1	£4	£8/£20
1860	Bronze proof		- - -	- - -	- - -	£175
1860	TB 5 berries	P1859	20p	£1	£3	£7/£18

★1856 Also described as E over R.
Either R was struck over an
incorrect E, or E was wrongly
selected to overstrike an
unsatisfactory R.
(or ?)

Date   Mintage   Peck   Fine   V.F.   E.F.   Unc/FDC

VICTORIA (continued)   DATE BELOW BRITANNIA - 20mm

Date	Mintage	Peck	Fine	V.F.	E.F.	Unc/FDC
1861	8,601,600	P1860	75p	£2	£8	£16/£24
1861	Bronze proof	(Cooke 1991)		choice	FDC	---/£165
1861	Obv. 3 (5 berries)		35p	£1.50	£5	£12/£20
1861	Date has small '8'		65p	£2.50	£4.50	£12/---
1862	14,336,000	P1865	50p	£1.80	£4	£12/£25
1862	Proof		---	---	£200	---/---
1862	Large 8 over small 8		(1990)		£30	---/---
1863	1,433,600	P1867	£10	£25	£50	£125/£250
1864	2,508,800	P1869	£1	£3	£6	£20/£40
1864	Angled horizontal bar to 4		---	£7	£12	£30/£60
1864	COPPER see P1589			Date Below Head on page 7		
1865	4,659,200	P1873	£1	£3.50	£8	£15/£30
1865	5 over 2	P1872A	£1	£3	£12	£25/£60
1865	5 over 3	---	£1	£4	£14	£20/£35
1865	Date has small '8'		£1.20	£3.75	£6.50	£15/---
1866	3,584,000	P1875 (D.Mason 1990) 75% lus. £6				Full £30
1866	Sixes close together		50p	£1.50	£4.50	£10/£15
1867	5,017,600	P1878	£1	£3	£8	£18/£35
1868	4,851,208	P1881	£1	£2	£6	£16/£24
1868	Bronze proof	P1882	---	---	---	£145/£250
1869	3,225,600	P1884	£1.25	£6	£15	£25/£55
1872	2,150,400	P1885	£1	£3	£6	£15/£30
1873	3,225,620	P1886	50p	£2	£5	£15/£25
1873	Low set 3 in date		---	---	£8	£16/£30

Proofs also occur for 1861, 1862, 1863, 1866, 1867.

OBVERSE 4 'AGED' (MATRONLY) BUST - still 'BUN' HEAD
H (centred below date) = Heaton Mint

Date	Mintage	Peck	Fine	V.F.	E.F.	Unc/FDC
1874H	3,584,000	P1887	45p	£2	£6	£12/£18
1874H	Bronze proof	(noted 1991)		about FDC		---/£170
1874H	Gs struck over Ʊ s		£50	£120	£240	£425/---
1875	712,760	P1890	£5	£10	£22	£55/---
1875	Large date	(5 berries)		£12	£25	£50/£90
1875	Small date	(5 berries)		£22	£45	£100/£300
1875	Small date	(4 berries)		£25	£50	£175/£350
1875H	6,092,800	P1892	25p	75p	£5	£10/£24
1876H	1,175,200	P1894	£4	£9	£25	£40/£96
1876	RF.G for REG		£5	---	---	---/---
1877	Proofs only	P1895	bronze	(Cooke '91)		£2400
1877	Bronzed proof		guesstimate			£1400/£1600
1878	4,008,540	P1896	25p	75p	£5	£10/£22
1878	Proof	P1897	---	---	---	--/£325
1879	3,977,180	P1898	25p	75p	£5	£10/£22
1879	Date has large '9'		£1	£4	£8	£12/£25
1880	1,842,710 4 berries	P1899	£1	£3	£9	£12/£25
1880	3 berries	P1901	£2	£20	£40	£60/£100

Proofs, in bronze, for all except 1876H and 1879.

The earliest legal farthings were made in 1613 under Royal Licence purchased from King James I by Lord Harington. 'Haringtons', and other Royal Farthings, have a harp reverse and the contraction 'HIB'. These are catalogued in "COLLECTORS COINS: IRELAND".

Date	Mintage	Peck	Fine	V.F.	E.F.	Unc/abt. FDC

VICTORIA continued - mainly obverse 5 - BRONZE

Date	Mintage	Peck	Fine	V.F.	E.F.	Unc/abt. FDC
1881	See below Obv.4	P1901 [A]	£20	£30	£40	£80/£120
1881	3,494,670 Obv.5	P1902	50p	£2	£4	£9/£20
1881H	1,792,000	P1904	£1	£3	£6	£12/£22
1882H	1,792,000	P1905	75p	£2	£7	£14/---
1883	1,128,680	P1907	£2	£4	£16	£25/£40
1884	5,782,000	P1909	15p	50p	£1	£5/£15
1885	5,442,308	P1911	25p	£1	£2	£5/£15
1886	7,767,790	P1913	25p	£1	£2	£5/£15
1887	1,340,800	P1915	£1	£2	£7	£16/£30
1888	1,887,250	P1916	75p	£1	£5	£12/£25
1890	2,133,070	P1917	75p	£1	£5	£12/£25
1891	4,959,690	P1919	40p	£1	£4	£9/£15
1892	887,240	P1921	£3	£5	£10	£25/£40
1893	3,904,320	P1923	50p	£1	£4	£15/£25
1893	Narrower date		£1	£2	£5	£15/£25
1894	2,396,770	P1924	50p	£1	£6	£9/£18
1895	2,852,852	P1925	£3	£8	£20	£30/£60

Proofs occur except 1881H, 1887, 1888,1893, 1895.

VICTORIA   'Old' or 'Widow' Head

Date	Mintage	Peck	Fine	V.F.	E.F.	Unc/abt. FDC
1895	Inc above	P1958	25p	£1	£4	£8/£16
1896	3,668,610	P1959	25p	£1	£3	£4/£8
1896	Noted		(Full lustre, quite exceptional)			£12.50
1897	4,579,800:		blackened to distinguish from half-sovereign			
1897	Undarkened	P1961	£1	£3	£10	£20/£35
1897	Horizon as P1961 but black finish		---	---		£12/£18
1897	Higher horizon	P1962	25p	£1	£3	£5/£9
1898	4,010,080	P1963	25p	£1	£4	£8/£12
1899	3,864,616	P1964	25p	£1	£4	£8/£12
1900	5,969,317	P1965	25p	60p	£2	£4/£8
1901	8,016,459	P1966	15p	35p	£1	£2/£4

Proofs occur for 1896 and, possibly, for 1901

Obverse 4 has 4 berries in wreath arranged as two pairs (2+2 and not 1+2+1 as previously). Obverse 5 has 3 berries arranged 2+1.

The prefix 'P' e.g. P1966 indicates that the number is a "Peck" number: that is the number allotted to the coin by C. Wilson Peck in the British Museum's famous coin 'bible' entitled - "ENGLISH COPPER, TIN and BRONZE COINS in the BRITISH MUSEUM".

FARTHINGS

Date	Mintage		Fine	V.F.	BRONZE E.F.	abt Unc./FDC
EDWARD VII						
1902	5,125,120		20p	£1	£3	£6/£12
1903 ★	5,331,200	★ low horizon	30p	£1	£3	£9/£12
1904	3,628,800		75p	£2	£4	£9/£14
1905	4,076,800		20p	£1	£4	£9/£14
1906	5,340,160		20p	75p	£3	£9/£14
1907	4,399,360		25p	£1	£4	£9/£14
1908	4,264,960		20p	50p	£4	£9/£14
1909	8,852,480		15p	45p	£3	£10/£14
1910	2,598,400		£1	£2	£5	£14/£21

All chemically darkened to avoid confusion with gold.

Date	Mintage		V.F.	E.F.	Unc./abt. FDC
GEORGE V		ALL DARKENED, CHEMICALLY, UNTIL 1918			
1911	5,196,800	(see foot of page)	£1	£3.50	£6/£9
1912	7,669,760		40p	£1.50	£5/£7
1913	4,184,320		65p	£1.50	£5/£7
1914	6,126,988	BRITT obv 1	65p	£3	£9/£12
1914		BRIT T obv 2	65p	£3	£9/£12
1915		BRITT	(no transactions noted)		
1915	7,129,254	BRIT T	65p	£3	£5/£12
1916	10,993,325		25p	£1	£3/£6
1917	21,434,844		15p	£1	£3/£4
1918	19,362,818	left bright	15p	£1	£2/£3
1918	Rare darkened finish		- - -	£6	£10/£15
1919	15,089,425		20p	£1	£2/£5
1920	11,480,536		20p	80p	£2/£5
1921	9,469,097		20p	80p	£2/£5
1922	9,956,983		20p	£1	£3/£6
1923	8,034,457		25p	£1	£3/£5
1924	8,733,414		25p	£1	£3/£6
1925	12,634,697		20p	£1	£3/£5
1926	9,792,397		20p	75p	£3/£6
1927	7,868,355		15p	50p	£2/£4
1928	11,625,600		15p	75p	£2/£3.50
1929	8,419,200		15p	75p	£2/£4
1930	4,195,200		15p	£1	£2/£4
1931	6,595,200		15p	£1	£2/£5.50
1931	Bronze proof		- - -	- - -	/£225
1932	9,292,800		15p	50p	£2/£3
1932	Bronze proof		- - -	- - -	/£235
1933	4,560,000		20p	£1	£2/£5
1933	Proof (Peck 2353)		- - -	(1988)	£165
1934	3,052,800		25p	£1.50	£4/£7
1934	Proof (Peck 2355)		- - -	(1988)	£165
1935	2,227,200		65p	£3	£6/£12
1936	9,734,400	★ issued posthumously	15p	25p	£1/£2.50

'Fine' are sold, usually from 'The Tray' 5p to 25p

EDWARD VIII   Duke of Windsor

1937   Extremely rare - not issued for general circulation see page 49

GEORGE V
1911   The 'standard' Peck obverse 1 has two variations:
                Obverse 1a = above B.M. the neck is hollow.
                Obverse 1b = above B.M. the neck is flat.
         At present, values are identical even amongst dealers who
      DO distinguish the variety - many don't; but more are doing so.

Date	Mintage		Peck No.	V.F.	E.F.	abt. Unc/FDC

GEORGE VI

Date	Mintage		Peck No.	V.F.	E.F.	Unc/FDC
1937	8,131,200		---		40p	£1/£2
1937	26,402	proofs	---		---	£4/£6
1938	7,449,600		---	20p	50p	£3/£6
1939	31,440,000		---	---	15p	45p/65p
1940	18,360,000		---		25p	80p/£2
1941	27,312,000		---		20p	60p/95p
1942	28,857,600		---		20p	75p/£1
1943	33,345,600		---		20p	60p/95p
1944	25,137,600		---		15p	45p/65p
1945	23,736,000		---		15p	45p/65p
1946	24,364,800		---	---	15p	60p/90p
1946	Bronze proof		P2476	(possibly 3 only) (1991)		£225
1947	14,745,600		---	---	15p	60p/90p
1948	16,622,400		---		15p	60p/95p
1949	8,424,000		---		20p	75p/£2
1950	10,324,800		---		15p	60p/£1
1950	17,513	proofs	---		---	£3/£5
1951	14,016,000		---		15p	40p/75p
1951	20,000	proofs	---		---	£3/£5
1952	5,251,200		---		15p	60p/95p
1952	Bronze proof		P2488		---	£125/£175

ELIZABETH II

Date	Mintage		Peck No.	V.F.	E.F.	Unc/FDC
1953	6,131,037:					
1953	Obv 1 Rev A		P2520	Currency Set		50p/£1.50
1953	Obv 1 Rev B		P2520A	---	---	£10/£20
1953	Obv 2 Rev A		P2520B	---	---	£15/£30
1953	Obv 2 Rev B		P2521	---	25p	75p/£1
1953	40,000 proofs		P2522 (of P2521)		---	£3/£6
1954	6,566,400		---	---	15p	25p/70p
1955	5,779,200		---	---	18p	30p/65p
1956	1,996,800		---	---	30p	50p/75p

Obverse 1 is poorly defined - the cross points TO a border bead.
Obverse 2 is sharper - the cross points BETWEEN two border beads.
   Reverse A (dies of George VI) - 'F' points BETWEEN two beads.
   Reverse B is similar but the 'F' points TO a border bead.

1953	Obverse/Reverse Rarity Scale	1 + A (C)	2 + A (R)
		1 + B (R)	2 + B (VC)
(R) = Rare	(C) = Common		(VC) = Very Common

Date	Details	Fine	V.F.	E.F.	abt. Unc/FDC

GEORGE III *Tower - London - Mint*   COPPER 29 mm

Date	Details	Fine	V.F.	E.F.	Unc/FDC
1770	Armoured Bust	£2	£10	£45	£85/£150
1770	No stop reverse P893A	---	---	---	---
1770	P894 and P895	Proofs in silver, and in copper			
1771	P896	£2	£10	£45	£70/£110
1771	P897 no stop reverse	---	£10	£45	£90/£130
1771	P898 ball below spear head		---	£40	£80/£120
1772	P899 and P902	£2	£10	£35	£75/£115
1772	P900 GEORIVS (error)	£4	£15	£50	£110/£160
1772	P901 ball below spear head		---	£40	£80/£120
1772	P903 no stop reverse	---	£10	£45	£90/£130
1773	P904	£2	£9	£30	£60/£90
1773	P905 no stop after REX	---	£9	£40	£80/£120
1773	P906 no stop reverse	---	£12	£50	£90/£140
1774	P907	£3	£10	£35	£65/£100
1775	P908	£3	£14	£45	£85/£130
1788	P966 Gilt proof	---	---	---	£195
1795	P1044 Cartwheel Pattern	(abtEF £99 1989) ---			

Soho - Birmingham - Mint

DATE BELOW BRITANNIA   COPPER 30 mm

Date	Details		Fine	V.F.	E.F.	Unc/FDC
1797	Pattern	P1154	---	£135	(1988)	---
1799	Gilt proof	P1156	---	---	---	FDC £340
1799	Bronzed proof	P1234	---	---	---	FDC £75
1799	Bronzed proof	P1247	---	---	---	£110/---
1799	5 incuse gunports	P1248	£1	£3	£15	£25/£45
1799	6 raised gunports	P1249	£1	£3	£15	£25/£45
1799	Plain hull	P1251	£1	£5	£20	£40/£60
1799	9 raised gunports	P1250	£1	£4	£18	£38/£55
1799	Raised line, no gunports	P1252	£5	£20	£45/£60	

DATE BELOW HEAD   COPPER 29 mm

Date	Details	Fine	V.F.	E.F.	Unc/FDC
1806	Olive branch, no berries	---	£2	£10	£40/£65
1806	Proof (almost superb FDC - full colour)	(1991)			£150/---
1806	3 berries, Soho underlined		£3	£12	£42/£68
1807	3 berries etc.	£1	£4	£16	£45/£70

SOHO MINT halfpennies have an edge milled in a deep groove; this gives the appearance of two halfpennies joined together.

Date	Mintage	Fine	V.F.	E.F.	Unc/FDC
GEORGE IV		LAUREATE HEAD		COPPER 28mm	
1825	215,040	£4	£16	£35	£50/£85
1825	Proof	--	---	---	---/£150
1826	9,031,630 Rev A	£2	£6	£20	£40/£60
1826	Rev B	--	£8	£30	£75/£105
1826	Proof Rev B	--	--	£75	£100/----
1827	5,376,000	£1	£4	£30	£50/£80
	Rev A; Saltire of shield has two incuse lines P1433				
	Rev B; Saltire of shield has one raised line P1436				
WILLIAM IV		BARE HEAD		COPPER 28mm	
1831	806,400	£1.25	£6	£30	£95/£125
1831	Proofs, bronzed	---	---	---	£95/----
1834	537,600	£1.25	£6	£30	£95/£125
1837	349,400	£1	£5	£20	£60/£90
VICTORIA Young Head DATE BELOW HEAD COPPER					
1838	456,960	50p	£2	£15	£45/£65
1839	Proofs, bronzed	---	--	---	£80/---
1839	Proofs, bronzed, inverted reverse	---	---	---	£120/£150
1841	1,075,200	50p	£2	£10	£20/£45
1841	Proofs, bronzed	---	---	---	£90/----
1843	967,680	£3	£10	£35	£90/£130
1844	1,075,200	£1	£4	£25	£60/£85
1845	1,075,200	£16	£45	£160	£225/£375
1846	860,160	£2	£5	£25	£65/£90
1847	752,640	£2	£5	£25	£65/£90
1848	322,560	£1	£5	£25	£65/£90
1848 ★	8 struck over 7	---	£3	£15	£45/£65
1848	8 struck over 3	---	£12	£30	---/---
1851	215,040 (no dots)	---	£4	£12	£40/£55
1851	Shield, 7 incuse dots	---	£4	£15	£65/---
1852	637,056 (no dots)	---	£4	£15	£60/£75
1852	Shield, 7 incuse dots	---	£4	£15	£60/£80
1853	1,559,040	45p	£2	£7	£20/£30
1853	3 over 2	£3	£9	£18	£25/£45
1853	Proofs, bronzed, inverted reverse	---	---	---	---/£200
1853	Copper proof	(Colin Cooke 1991)			---/£220
1854	12,354,048 ?	£1	£2	£8	£15/£25
1855	1,455,837	£1	£2	£8	£30/£45
1856	1,942,080	£1	£4	£20	£40/£60
1857	1,182,720 (no dots)	---	£3	£15	£45/---
1857	Shield, 7 incuse dots	---	£2	£10	£50/£65
1858	2,472,960	50p	£3	£14	£36/---
	noted	(Seaby 1989 GEF £15)			
1858	Smaller date	£1	£3	£20	£46/---
1858	8 over 6	£2	£6	£15	£30/£50
1858	8 over 7	£1	£3	£9	£20/£30
1859	1,290,340	£1	£3	£14	£40/---
1859	9 struck over 8	£2	£6	£25	£45/---
1860 ★★	Extremely rare	£175	£500	£2200	£4000/---
1860 ★★	Extremely rare Proof	(1988)		EF+ £2700	----

★ Variety more common than correctly dated piece
★★ Date is below head, not below Britannia

		Date	Mintage	Fine	V.F.	E.F.	abt. Unc/FDC

VICTORIA "Bun" Head DATE BELOW BRITANNIA

TYPE 1: BEADED BORDERS :

Date	Mintage	Fine	V.F.	E.F.	abt. Unc/FDC
1860	1 + A (P1750)	--	£2	£12	£20/£40
	noted (Seaby 1990 EF some lustre £16)	---			
	noted (Cooke 1990 BU full lustre £32)	---			
1860	1 + A (P1751/52/53 Proofs bronze and bronzed				

TYPE 2: TOOTHED BORDERS :
Obv 2 has 7 berries. Obv 3 has 4 berries, all leaves have raised mid-ribs.
Obv 4 has 4 berries, but four leaves have double incuse lines to mid-ribs.
  Lighthouse :   B tapering, pointed   C cylindrical with rounded top.

1860	2 + B (P1754)	--	£2	£12	£25/£40
1860	3 + B (P1756)	--	£3	£15	£40/£60
1860	3 + C (P1757)	--	£3	£15	£40/£55
1860	4 + B (P1758)	£2	£6	£18	£50/£75
1860★	F of HALF struck over P (The Rawcliffe Halfpenny)				
	--	$60 (£25 1987)			---/---
1861	54,118,400 Ten obv/rev combinations + proofs				
1861	Without signature	50p	£2	£10	£15/£25
1861	Signature on rock	£1	£3	£15	£20/£35

  ★ FARTHINGS of this date bear Fs with little or no lower serif
to the lower horizontal bar (illustr.) Perhaps the first halfpennies
were struck with the same, or a similar, type-face and, to avoid
having HALP PENNYs as well as PARTHINGS were overstruck.

Date	Mintage		Fine	V.F.	E.F.	Unc/FDC
VICTORIA		DATE BELOW BRITANNIA			BRONZE 26 mm	
1862	61,107,200:					
	L.C.W. on rock		£1	£3	£10	£20/£30
1862	Proof	P1775	--	--	---	£200
1862	No L.C.W.	P1776	--	£2	£8	£15/£25
1862	Proof	P1777	--	---	£200	---
1862	A, B, or C to left of lighthouse			£360/£500		
1862	Unbarred A i.e Λ		£120	---	---	---/---
1863	15,948,800		75p	£2	£12	£30/£45
1864	537,600		£2	£5	£20	£35/£50
1865	8,064,000		£2	£5	£20	£35/£50
1865	5 over 3		£12	£50	£140	£265/£400
1866	2,508,800		£1	£4	£15	£25/£36
1867	2,508,806		£2	£5	£20	£36/£55
1868	3,046,400		£1	£4	£24	£36/---
1868	Cupro-nickel proof				(Seaby 1989 FDC £120)	
1869	3,225,600		--	£4	£20	£60/£95
1870	4,350,739		£1	£4	£24	£36/---
1871	1,075,280 ?		£12	£30	£85	£150/---
1872	4,659,410		£1	£4	£24	£36/---
1873	3,404,880		£1	£5	£25	£40/---
1874	1,347,665		£3	£14	£50	£85/---
1874	Portrait as 1874H		£1	£4	£24	£36/---
1874H	5,017,600		£1	£4	£20	£32/---
1875	5,430,815		65p	£2	£16	£25/---
1875H	1,254,400		£2	£6	£25	£40/---
1876H	6,809,600		65p	£2	£16	£25/£45
1877	5,209,505		65p	£2	£16	£25/£45
1878	1,425,535		£2	£12	£36	£70/£140
1879	3,582,545		60p	£2	£12	£20/---
1880	2,423,465		£1	£5	£20	£30/£45
1881	2,007,515		£1	£5	£20	£30/£45
1881H	1,792,000		75p	£3	£15	£20/£35
1882H	4,480,000		75p	£3	£15	£20/£35
1883	3,000,725		75p	£4	£20	£28/---
1884	6,989,580		60p	£2	£12	£24/---
1885	8,600,574		60p	£2	£12	£24/£40
1886	8,586,155		50p	£2	£10	£20/£30
1887	10,701,305		50p	£1	£9	£20/£32
1888	6,814,070		35p	£1	£12	£18/---
1889	7,748,234		35p	£2	£12	£18/---
1889	9 over 8		£4	£20	£45	£90/---
1890	11,254,235		40p	£2	£8	£12/£25
1891	13,192,260		40p	£2	£8	£15/---
1892	2,478,335		£1	£2	£8	£20/£28
1893	7,229,344		40p	£2	£6	£12/£22
1894	1,767,635		75p	£3	£10	£24/£36

Date	Mintage		Fine	V.F.	E.F.	Unc/abt FDC

VICTORIA — Veiled, Old, or Widow Head

Date	Mintage		Fine	V.F.	E.F.	Unc/abt FDC
1895	3,032,154	P1950	30p	£1	£4	£9/£15
1896	9,142,500	P1951	25p	90p	£3	£8/£12
1897	8,690,315	P1951A	30p	£1	£4	£10/£15
1897	Horizon higher	P1952	- - -	90p	£3	£8/£12
1898	8,595,180	P1953	35p	£1	£4	£10/£15
1899	12,108,001	P1954	20p	60p	£3	£7/£12
1900	13,805,190	P1955	- - -	60p	£2	£5/£9
1901	11,127,360	P1956	- - -	- - -	£2	£3/£5

EDWARD VII

Date	Mintage	Fine	V.F.	E.F.	Unc/abt FDC
1902	13,672,960	- - -	- - -	£3	£7/£10
1902	LOW TIDE variety	£2	£8	£32	£50/£80
1903	11,450,880	- - -	£1	£5	£15/£21
1904	8,131,200	- - -	£2	£8	£20/£28
1905	10,124,800	- - -	£1	£5	£14/£22
1906	11,101,440	- - -	£1	£4	£8/£12
1907	16,849,280	- - -	£1	£4	£8/£12
1908	16,620,800	- - -	£1	£5	£18/£24
1909	8,279,040	- - -	£1.50	£8	£20/£28
1910	10,769,920	- - -	£1	£5	£10/£16

Proofs exist for 1902; they are very rare.

"LOW TIDE" VARIETY referred to above and on page 26 may be determined thus: if the horizon meets Britannia at the point, below the knee, where right and left legs cross; NORMAL tide is indicated. If, however, the horizon meets Britannia at a much lower point - nearer the hem of her drape - then a LOW TIDE variety has been detected.

abt.

Date	Mintage		Fine	V.F.	E.F.	Unc/FDC
GEORGE V		BRITANNIA REVERSE			BRONZE 26mm	
1911	12,570,880	1911 Obverse 1a - the	£1	£3		£7/£10
1912	21,185,920	neck is hollow	£1	£3		£7/£10
1913	17,476,480	Obverse 1b - the	£1	£5		£12/£18
1914	20,289,111	neck is flat	£1	£4		£9/£12
1915	21,563,040	(See note on page 11)	£1	£4		£9/£12
1916	39,386,143			70p	£4	£7/£10
1917	38,245,436	- - -		60p	£3	£7/£10
1918	22,321,072	- - -		60p	£3	£7/£10
1919	28,104,001	- - -		60p	£3	£7/£10
1920	35,146,793	- - -		60p	£3	£7/£10
1921	28,027,293	- - -		60p	£2	£6/£10
1922	10,734,964	- - -		£1.25	£4	£8/£12
1923	12,266,282	- - -		65p	£4	£7/£10
1924	13,971,038	- - -		65p	£4	£8/£12
1925	12,216,123	Head as for 1924		90p	£5	£9/£15
1925	Modified Head	as for 1926		£1.50	£8	£12/£20
1926	6,712,306	- - -		£1	£6	£10/£15
1927	15,589,622	- - -		55p	£3	£7/£10
	SMALLER HEAD:					
1928	20,935,200	- - -		40p	£2	£3/£6
1928	Proof	- - -		(Spink 1988)		- -/£175
1929	25,680,000	- - -		30p	£2	£3/£6
1930	12,532,800	- - -		30p	£2	£3/£6
1931	16,137,600	- - -		30p	£2	£3/£6
1932	14,448,000	- - -		30p	£2	£3/£6
1933	10,560,000	- - -		30p	£2	£4/£7
1934	7,704,000	- - -		40p	£2.50	£4/£9
1935	12,180,000	- - -		30p	£2	£4/£8
1936	23,008,800	- - -			£1	£2/£4

Proofs 1926 to 1936 inclusive: British Museum

1911   Some dies were punched with date close to line of exergue (segment containing date) = Rev A

Clear gap = Rev B

Combinations:

1a + A   1a + B
1b + A   1b + B
1912   A   and   B

Date	Mintage	Fine	V.F.	E.F.	Unc/abt. FDC

EDWARD VIII *(Duke of Windsor)*   Reverse GOLDEN HIND

| 1937 | Excessively rare | | | See pages 48 and 49 | |

GEORGE VI   Reverse GOLDEN HIND

1937	24,504,000	---	---	65p	£1/£2
1937	26,402 proofs		---	FDC	£4.50
1938	40,320,000	---	10p	£1	£2/£3
1938	Noted (D. Mason 1990) BU 100% lustre				--/£3
1939	28,924,800		10p	£1.50	£2/£3
1940	32,162,400		30p	£2	£3/£5
1941	45,120,000		5p	45p	£1/£2
1942	17,908,800		5p	45p	£1.50/£3
1943	76,200,000		10p	50p	£1/£2.50
1944	81,840,000		5p	45p	£1/£2.50
1945	57,000,000		5p	70p	£1.50/£2.50
1946	22,725,600		30p	£2.25	£4/£6
1947	21,266,400		10p	£1	£3/£4
1948	26,947,200	---	10p	45p	£1/£2
1949	24,744,000	---	10p	90p	£1/£3
1950	24,153,600	---	10p	45p	£1/£2
1950	17,513 proofs	---	---	---	£2.50/£4
1951	14,868,000	---	20p	£1.20	£4/£5
1951	20,000 proofs	---	---	---	£2.50/£4
1952	33,278,400	---	10p	25p	50p/£1

Box (centre, at 1940):
1940
★ ★ ★ ★
L   P   = Rev A
★ ★ ★ ★
L   P   = Rev B
★
L   = Rev C
See 'pointings' page 65

ELIZABETH II   Cross points BETWEEN rim beads   ★ ★ / + = Obverse 1

  Cross points TO a rim bead   ★ ★ ★ / + = Obverse 2

1953	8,910,000 :				
1953	Obverse 1	---	---	---	£2.50
1953	Obverse 2	---	10p	20p	50p/£1
1953	40,000 proofs			FDC	£3
1954	19,375,200	---	10p	£1	£3/£4
1955	18,465,600	---	10p	£1	£2/£3
1956	21,799,200	---	---	£1	£3/£4
1957	39,672,000	---	---	20p	£1
1957	Variety has a calm sea	---	---	£2	£6.50
1958	66,331,200	---	---	---	50p
1958	Proof	(noted 1990)		---	---/£65
1959	79,176,000	---	---	---	25p
1960	41,340,000	---	---	---	30p/60p
1961	Decimal Patterns see page 88	---	---	---	---
1962	41,779,200	---	---	---	15p/50p
1963	42,720,000	---	---	---	10p/20p
1964	78,583,200	---	---	---	10p
1965	98,083,200	---	---	---	10p
1966	95,289,600	---	---	---	5p/12p
1967	146,490,400	---	---	---	5p/12p

Total for 1967 includes 46,226,400 struck in 1968

| 1970 | 750,424   LAST STERLING Proofs (1971/75) | | | | £1 |

1925/27   Effigy modified to aid striking, all coins
1928   Smaller head, for halfpennies and pennies
1949   IND:IMP (Emperor of India) discontinued, all coins
1954   BRITT:OMN discontinued - all coins
1969   Halfpenny demonetized - 1st August

					abt.
Date	Mintage	Fine	V.F.	E.F.	Unc/FDC

GEORGE III   *SOHO (Birmingham) MINT*

THE CARTWHEEL PENNY:

DATE STRUCK INTO BROAD RIM   COPPER 36mm

1797	10 leaves in wreath	£4	£12	£40	£100/£150
1797	11 leaves in wreath	£4	£14	£50	£150/£200
1797	Bronzed proof	Auction(1988)			£175

DATE BELOW HEAD   COPPER 34mm

Deep groove to edge suggests two joined coins:

1806	Incuse curl right of knot	---	£7	£18	£25/£40
1806	No incuse hair curl	(Seaby 1990)		GEF £65	----
1806	P1325 Gilt proof (1990) GEF Full Gilt			£135 ---	
1806	P1327 Copper proof	---	---	---	£175
1806	P1333 Bronzed proof (1990)		abt EF £50		----
1806	P1349 Copper re-strike proof	---	---	---	£160
1807	P1344	---	£7	£15	£30/£50
1808	One example known (Spink 1985)	---	---	--- Mint	£15,000
	Varieties, proofs, patterns; extensive.				

SOHO
(Birmingham)
PENNY

GEORGE IV   *ROYAL (Tower) MINT*   COPPER 34mm

1825	1,075,200 P1420	£3	£14	£45	£125/£170
1825	Proofs	---	---	---	£180
1826	5,913,000 P1422	£2	£10	£36	£95/£150
1826	St Andrew's Cross varieties:				
	Thin raised line		£12	£40	£100/£160
	Thick raised line		£16	£50	£120/£185
1826	Proofs: plain, varieties, bronzed	---	---	£100/£150	
1827	1,451,520 Fair £15	£35	£85	£950	£1,500
1827	Noted (1991) GVF - no corrosion £290				----

WILLIAM IV   COPPER 34mm

1831	806,400 P1455	£4	£24	£70	£140/£250
1831	Bronzed proofs	---	---	£90	£135/£200
1831	.W.W incuse initials	---	£30	£120	£300
1831	W.W. incuse initials	---	£34	£150	£325
1834	322,560	£6	£24	£90	£175/£300
1837	174,720	£8	£40	£125	£245/£365

"CARTWHEEL"
PENNY

"CARTWHEEL" TWOPENCES

abt.

Date	Mintage	Fine	V.F.	EF/GEF	Unc/FDC

GEORGE III

DATE STRUCK INTO BROAD RIM   COPPER 41mm

Date	Mintage	Fine	V.F.	EF/GEF	Unc/FDC
1797	722,160	£5	£18	£60/£110	£200/£300
1797	Bronzed proofs	---	---	---	£300/£400
1797	¼d, ½d, 1d, 2d set			£850	(Spink 1986)

These were the first coins (copper currency) to bear the initials D:G:
(DEI GRATIA : "BY THE GRACE OF GOD"). Designed by Küchler, they
were struck on steam powered presses installed by James Watt at the
Soho, Birmingham, refineries of Matthew Boulton.

"8 of these shall weigh 1lb and measure one foot"

A break in the rising-face-value order has been made because this huge
coin belongs with the very similar Küchler pennies. Weighing over 60
grams for each twopence, with 120 to the £1 (240 pence to £1), could
you lift your weekly income if you were paid in Cartwheels?

Date	Mintage	Peck	Fine	V.F.	E.F.	abt. Unc/FDC

VICTORIA Young Head

COPPER 34mm
DATE BELOW HEAD

Date	Mintage		Peck	Fine	V.F.	E.F.	abt. Unc/FDC
1839	Bronzed proof		1479	DEF : o.t.		- - -	£185/£250
1841	913,920	REG:	1480	£5	£17	£48	£150/£200
1841	Proofs			- - -	- - -	- - -	£250
1841	Proof in silver		(1980	As Struck)		- - -	£1,500
1841	No colon	REG	1484	£1	£5	£15	£22/£50
1843	483,830	REG:	1486	£15	£70	£220	£350/- - - -
1843	No colon	REG	1485	£18	£75	£250	£450/- - - -
1844	215,040		1487	£3	£7	£24	£60/£90
1845	322,560		1489	£4	£14	£50	£80/£130
1846	483,840	DEF :	1490	£3	£9	£40	£75/£110
1846		DEF:	1491	£4	£10	£46	£80/£125
1847	430,080	DEF:	1492	£2	£7	£30	£65/£100
1847		DEF :	1493	£2	£7	£30	£65/£100
1848	161,280		1496	£2	£7	£30	£60/£95
1848	8 over 6		1494	- -	£22	£65	£120/£185
1848	8 over 7		1495	- -	£5	£24	£75/£110
1849	268,800		1497	£25	£85	£250	£500/- - - -
1851	432,224	DEF :	1498	£3	£7	£35	£90/£125
1851		DEF:	1499	£4	£12	£35	£120/£165
1853	1,021,440	DEF :	1500	60p	£3	£12	£20/£40
1853	Narrow date			- - -	- - -	£12	£20/£40
1853	Proofs - copper and bronzed					- - -	£250
1853		DEF:	1503	£1	£6	£25	£75/£110
1853	Plain trident		1504	£2	£12	£30	£60/£90
1854	4 over 3		1505	£15	£45	£60	£100/£160
1854	6,720,000 p.t.		1506	£1	£4	£15	£25/£60
1854	Ornam trident		1507	- - -	£2	£9	£15/£35
1855	5,273,866 o.t.		1508	- - -	£4	£15	£25/£60
1855	Plain trident		1509	- - -	£3	£12	£20/£45
1856	1,212,288 DEF:		p.t.	£9	£42	£90	£300/£375
1856	Plain trident proof		- - -	- - -	- - -	- - -	£250
1856		DEF :	o.t.	£5	£35	£80	£250/£350
1857	752,640	DEF:	p.t.	£1	£5	£15	£30/£50
1857		DEF :	o.t.	£1	£5	£15	£30/£50
1857	Smaller date		p.t.	£1	£5	£15	£30/£50
1858	1,559,040:						
	8 over 3		1515	- -	£22	£45	£90/- - -
	8 over 6			- -	- - -	£60	- - -
	8 over 7		1516	- -	£3	£14	£35/- - -
	Smaller date		1517	£1	£4	£16	£42/- - -
	Large date no W.W.	1518	65p	£3	£12	£25/£50
1859	1,075,200 Large date		£1	£6	£20	£60/£90
1859	9 over 8			£4	£16	£42	£95/£130
1859	Smaller date			£2	£8	£25	£80/- - -
1859	Proof			- - -	- - -	- - -	£950
1860	60 struck over 59			£100	£300	£600	£850/- - -

It is not unusual for the range Unc/FDC to vary thus:
Some lustre £12; Good lustre £20; Much lustre £28; Full lustre £35
DEF: = near colon - DEF : = far colon - o.t. = ornamental trident
plain tridents have near colons   p.t. = plain trident

NEAR COLON:

FAR COLON :

P2119

P2050

BEADED

TOOTHED

P2064

selection of pattern pennies
with Peck Numbers.

VICTORIA
'Bun' Head - date below Britannia - 31mm

Rev	Peck	F.	V.F.	E.F.	Unc.	Rev	Peck	F.	V.F.	E.F.	Unc.
1860	5,053,440		BEADED RIM BORDER - Obv. L.C.WYON ON TRUNCATION								
A	1617	£2	£4	£18	£36	B	1621	silv. proof		(£500 EF+)	
B	1619	£4	£8	£30	£60	B	1622	bronzed proof	--	£250	
B	1620	extra heavy flan		£300		C	1623	£10	£45	£95	---
		A proof 1860 penny in gold				B	1620A	---	(1987)	£11,200	
		Mule beaded obverse/toothed reverse					1624	---	£90	£250	---
		Mule toothed obverse/beaded reverse					1628	---	---	£600	---
		Wyon Pattern MDCCCLX nickel-alloy 2051 (Seaby 1989 GEF £450)									

TOOTHED RIM/BORDER - L.C.WYON ON or BELOW TRUNCATION:

Rev	Peck	F.	V.F.	E.F.	Unc.	Rev	Peck	F.	V.F.	E.F.	Unc.
C★	1625	on £6	£25	£60		C★	1631	bronze proof	---	£250	
D	1626	on £15	£95	£225		C★	1632	below £6	£25	£60	
C★	1629	below ---	£25	---		C★	1633	no sig £35	£65	---	
C★	1630	heavy flan £150	---			C★	1635	no sig £35	£65	---	
		ONF PENNY variety: damaged die 1634 £35 fair (1988) ---									

Rev	Peck	F.	V.F.	E.F.	Unc.	Rev	Peck	F.	V.F.	E.F.	Unc.
1861	36,449,280:	L.C.WYON ON or BELOW TRUNCATION									
C★	1637	on £90	---	---		C★	1643	no sig £25	---	---	
F	1638	no sig £50	---	---		C★	1644	no sig ---	£20	---	
C★	1639	below ---	£18	---				6 over 8 £50	fair (1988)		
F	1642	no sig £20	fair (1988)	---		F	1646	no sig £5	£15	---	

OBVERSE 5 - NO SIGNATURE - WREATH OF 16 LEAVES - RAISED MIDRIBS
REVERSE F - NO SIGNATURE - THUMB DOES NOT TOUCH ST.GEORGE'S CROSS

Date	Mintage	F.	V.F.	E.F.	Unc.	Date	Mintage	F.	V.F.	E.F.	Unc.
1862	50,534,400	£1	£4	£16	£40	1865	5 over 3 £15	£45	£200	£425	
1862	Bronzed proof ---	---	---	£250		1865	Pattern bronze P2061	nrFDC	£300		
1862	Date from halfpenny die (smaller):					1866	9,999,360	£1	£6	£22	£55
	£60 fair (1988)	---				1867	5,483,520	£2	£9	£25	£75
1862	8 over 6 (Seaby 1989 GVF £275)					1868	1,182,720	£3	£18	£55	£125
1862	Pattern cu-nickel P2060 (FDC £600)					1868	Bronze proof P1681	---	£250		
1863	28,062,720	£1	£4	£20	£50	1868	Copper-nickel proof	£200	£365		
1863	Bronzed proof ---	---	---	£250		1869	2,580,480	£15	£65	£250	£525
1863	Die number below date:					1870	5,695,022	(Spink 1988 UNC £165)			
	3 below £100 (fair 1988)					1870		(Seaby 1989 EF £60)			
1864	3,440,646 Plain 4	£28	£125	£325		1871	1,290,318	£6	£45	£100	£225
1864	Crosslet 4	£45	£200	£425		1872	8,494,572	£1	£8	£30	£75
1865	8,601,600	£2	£9	£45	£90	1873	8,494,200	£1	£8	£30	£75

OBVERSE 5; and OBVERSE 6 (a MORE MATRONLY PORTRAIT)
REVERSE F; and REVERSE G (a LESS GRACEFUL BRITANNIA)

O/R	Peck	F.	V.F.	E.F.	Unc.	O/R	Peck	F.	V.F.	E.F.	Unc.
1874	5,621,86 :					**1874H**	6,666,240 :				
						5/F	1694	£1	£4	£20	£45
5/F	1690	£2	£10	£40	£75	5/G	1695	£2	£12	£45	£80
5/G	1691	£2	£10	£40	£75	6/F	1696	£1	£4	£20	£45
6/F	1692	£1	£8	£30	£65	6/G	1697	£1	£4	£18	£40
6/G	1693	£1	£8	£25	£60		1698	Bronze proof ---		£250	

1860 reverse: L.C.W. incuse below shield
Rev. A = crosses outlined with treble incuse lines, no rock
Rev. B = crosses outlined by close, double, raised lines, no rock
Rev. C = similar to Rev. B, but small rock to left of lighthouse
Rev. C★ = as Rev. C, but with minor modifications to rocks and sea
Rev. D = as Rev. C, but L.C.W. incuse below foot
Rev. E = no signature, thumb touches St. George's Cross; no vertical lines to lantern
Rev. F = no signature, thumb does not touch Cross, lantern has six vertical lines
Rev. G = Britannia has long, thin neck; her helmet is tall and narrow; a tall, thin lighthouse

VICTORIA   "BUN" HEAD   (continued)

Date	Mintage	F.	V.F.	E.F.	Unc.	Date	Mintage	F.	V.F.	E.F.	Unc.
1875	10,691,040	£1	£5	£16	£40	1882H	7,526,400	£1	£5	£16	£30
1875H	752,640	£8	£45	£150	£300	1883	6,237,438	£1	£6	£20	£45
1875H	Proof P1706	---		nFDC	£350	1884	11,702,802	£1	£3	£12	£30
1876H	11,074,560	£1	£5	£16	£30	1885	7,145,862	£1	£3	£12	£30
1877	9,624,747	£1	£5	£20	£35	1886	6,087,759	60p	£3	£14	£26
1877	Proof cupro-nickel			nFDC	£700	1887	5,315,085	60p	£3	£14	£26
1878	2,764,470	£2	£9	£30	£60	1887	Aluminium pattern (P2175)				£375
1878	Proof P1713	---		nFDC	£275	1888	5,125,020	60p	£3	£14	£30
1879	7,666,476	£1	£5	£16	£30	1889	12,559,737	50p	£3	£12	£25
1879	Re-touched Obv. P1715		£30		GEF	1889	Narrow date (P1745)			£25	---
1880	3,000,831	£2	£9	£40	£55	1890	15,330,840	50p	£3	£12	£25
1881	2,302,261	£2	£10	£42	£65	1891	17,885,961	30p	£2	£10	£16
1881	Portrait 'aged' further:					1892	10,501,671	30p	£2	£12	£20
	P1722	£2	£12	£50	£75	1893	8,161,737	40p	£3	£12	£22
1881H	3,763,200	£1	£5	£16	£30	1894	3,883,452	£2	£5	£15	£34
1881H	Heraldically coloured shield				£45	Proofs for 1881, 1884/85/86 and 1890/91/92					

OLD, VEILED, or WIDOW HEAD

Date	Mintage	F.	V.F.	E.F.	Unc.	Date	Mintage	F.	V.F.	E.F.	Unc.
1895	5,395,830 Rev B	£1	£5		£10	1897	Higher horizon (Spink'88)				£100
1895	No sea Rev A	£2	£15	£75	£165	1898	14,296,836	15p	£1	£4	£12
1895	Pattern (P2066)		nFDC	£720		1899	26,441,069	15p	£1	£4	£8
1896	24,147,156	15p	£1	£4	£8	1900	31,778,109	---	50p	£3	£6
1896	9 and 6 further apart	£1	£5		£9	1901	22,205,568	---	50p	£2	£4
1897	20,756,620	15p	£1	£4	£8						

1895 Rev A, trident to P is 2mm; no sea behind
1895 Rev B, trident to P is 1mm; sea behind (to left of) Britannia
1895 Pattern, only five known, (1985 FDC) £1200
Full lustre and/or abt.FDC can add 50% to Unc. value

Date	Mintage	Fine	V.F.	E.F.	Unc/FDC
EDWARD VII				BRONZE	31 mm
1902	26,976,768	40p	£1.25	£3	£8/£12
1902	LOW TIDE variety	£1	£4	£15	£30/£45
1903	21,415,296	---	£1	£8	£12/£21
1903	Open '3' Fair £30 (Spink 1988)	---		---	---/---
1904	12,913,152	---		£12	£18/£30
1905	17,783,808	---	£1.50	£10	£16/£25
1906	37,989,504	---	£1.50	£6	£12/£18
1907	47,322,240	---	£1.50	£6	£12/£18
1908	31,506,048	---	£1.50	£6	£12/£20
1909	19,617,024	---	£1	£6	£14/£20
1910	29,549,184	---	£1	£5	£10/£15
GEORGE V				BRONZE	31 mm
1911	23,079,168	(1 + A)	40p	£4	£8/£12
1911	Hollow neck (see page 11) (1988 GEF £20)				---
1912	48,306,048	(1 + A)	40p	£4	£8/£16
1912H	16,800,000	(1 + A)	£3	£20	£42/£60
1913	65,497,872	(2 + B)	75p	£5	£10/£20
1914	50,820,997	---	75p	£4	£10/£15
1915	47,310,807	---	£1	£5	£10/£15
1916	86,411,165	---	60p	£3	£9/£12
1917	107,905,436	---	60p	£3	£9/£12
1918	84,227,372	---	60p	£3	£6/£9
1918H	3,660,800	£1	£6	£65	£120/---
1918KN	Inc above	£2	£8	£75	£150/---
1919	113,761,090	---	60p	£3	£9/£12
1919H	5,209,600	£1	£5	£55	£110/£175
1919KN	Inc above	£2	£10	£90	£180/£225
1920	124,693,485	(2 + B)	45p	£3	£6/£10
1920	(P2259)	(3 + B)			---/---
1921	129,717,693	(2 + B)	45p	£3	£6/£12
1921	(P2261)	(3 + B)	45p	£3	£6/£12
1922	16,346,711	(3 + B)	£1.50	£10	£15/£30
1923 to 1925	None	---	---	---	---
1926	4,498,519	---	£2	£16	£20/£40
1926	Modified effigy	£3	£20	£200	£450/£650
1927	60,989,561	---	45p	£3	£4/£8
1928	50,178,000 smaller head	25p	£2	£3/£6	
1929	49,132,800	---	25p	£2	£3/£6
1930	29,097,600	---	45p	£4	£6/£9
1931	19,843,200	---	75p	£5	£10/£15
1932	8,277,600	---	£2	£15	£24/£40
1932	Proof (P2278)	---	nFDC	£150	
1933	8 (but see page 27)		£18,975 (1986)		
1933	Pattern by Lavrillier		(1986)		£4,100
1933	A uniface		(1980 £28,750)		£50,000
1934	13,965,600	---	£1	£5	£12/£22
1935	56,070,000	---	30p	£1	£2/£4
1935	Bronze proof	(1993)	---	FDC	£220
1936	154,296,000	---	---	£1	£2/£4

Proofs for all dates from 1926 to 1936 except 1933

Obv 1, bottom stop of colon close to A, GRA: BRITT

Obv 2, stops are midway but cramped, GRA:BRITT: farther apart

Obv 3, as Obv 2, but words BRITT: farther apart

Toothed circle of rev A has 163 teeth whilst B has 188

H-Heaton Mint Mark

KN-Kings Norton Mint Mark

1919

1913

ONE PENNY

1933

ONE PENNY

1933

P2279

P2284

In addition to the eight pennies listed on page 26 (left-hand pair above); there were patterns, possibly four, struck from dies engraved by Andre Lavrillier (right-hand pair above) having a 'military' King George V, a thick trident, and a sea of wavy lines. Yet another 1933 penny is uniface: having a "tail" but no "head" - the word MODEL appears instead. The 1933 set from St. Mary's Church, Hawksworth Wood, was offered for sale at Sotheby's in 1972. It fetched £7,000. This set was one of those placed under foundation stones laid by King George in 1933.

Date	Mintage	Fine	V.F.	E.F.	abt. Unc/FDC

EDWARD VIII (Duke of Windsor)

1937	Specimen strikings only - see pages 48 and 49				Bronze 31 mm

GEORGE VI
Bronze 31 mm

Date	Mintage	Fine	V.F.	E.F.	abt. Unc/FDC
1937	88,896,000	- - -	10p	50p	£1/£2
1937	26,402 proofs	- - -	- - -		/£5
1938	121,560,000	- - -	10p	65p	£1/£2
1939	55,560,000	- - -	30p	£1	£3/£5
1940	42,284,400	- - -	50p	£2	£5/£7
1941 to 1943 none		- - -	- - -	- - -	- - -
1944	42,600,000	- - -	30p	£2	£4/£6
1945	79,531,200	- - -	25p	£1	£3/£4
1945	Doubled 9	£1	£5	£25	- - -
1946	66,855,600	- - -	15p	£1	£2/£3
1947	52,220,400	- - -	15p	£1	£2/£3
1948	63,961,200	- - -	5p	25p	50p/£2
1949	14,324,400	- - -	10p	60p	£1/£2
1950	240,000	£2	£4	£6	£12/£18
1950	17,513 proofs	- - -	- - -	- - -	/£15
1951	120,000	£3	£6	£9	£18/£25
1951	20,000 proofs	- - -	- - -	- - -	£12/£15

Proofs for all dates except, possibly, 1947 ••••

1937	Rev Aa	Ns point to border teeth		NN ••••	
1937	Rev Ab	Ns point between teeth (b is rarer)		NN	
1940	Rev Ab	has single exergue line			
1940	Rev B	has double exergue line (Ab is rarer)			
1944	Rev Ba	waves touch exergue			
1944	Rev Bb	gap between waves and exergue			

————————————————————————— (POINTINGS - page 65)

ELIZABETH II
Bronze 31 mm

Date	Mintage	Fine	V.F.	E.F.	abt. Unc/FDC
1953	Pattern (not in Peck) unique ? : has toothed (not beaded) border				Spink £1,950
1953	1,308,400 (the 'Plastic' Set)	- - -		£1	£2/£4
1953	40,000 proofs	- - -	- - -		£5/£6
1953	Pattern from sand-blasted dies		- - -	£300	(1985)
1954	1 retrieved from change. Now in British Museum.				
1954	(Another, or the same one?) Purchased in 1992 for £21,000				
1955 to 1960 none		- - -	- - -	- - -	- - -
1961	48,313,400	- - -	- - -	- - -	25p/60p
1962	157,588,600	- - -	- - -	- - -	20p/50p
1963	119,733,600	- - -	- - -	- - -	- - -/15p
1964	153,294,000	- - -	- - -	- - -	12p/25p
1965	121,310,400	- - -	- - -	- - -	10p/20p
1965	In gold, unofficial, (Christies 1989)		- - -		£1300
1966	165,739,200	- - -	- - -	- - -	- - -/10p
1966	Exists with Jersey penny obverse	- - -	- - -	- - -	- - -
1967	155,280,000	- - -	- - -	- - -	- - -/10p
1968	170,400,000 all dated 1967				
1969	219,360,000 all dated 1967				
1970	109,524,000 all dated 1967: 654,564,000				

Proofs for some dates. 1970 proofs, from sets, £1/£2

THREE HALFPENCES ISSUED FOR COLONIAL USE

Date	Mintage	Fine	V.F.	E.F.	abt. Unc/FDC
WILLIAM IV		Silver 12 mm			
1834	800,448	45p	£2	£8	£16/£25
1835	633,600	70p	£3	£12	£24/£36
1835	5 struck over 4	£2	£10	£40	£80/- - -
1836	158,400	70p	£3	£12	£24/£36
1837	30,624	£4	£16	£65	£120/£180
VICTORIA		Silver 12 mm			
1838	538,560	60p	£3	£12	£25/£40
1839	760,320	35p	£2	£8	£18/£25
1840	95,040	£1	£5	£20	£36/£60
1841	158,400	50p	£2	£8	£16/£30
1842	1,869,120	50p	£2	£8	£16/£30
1843	475,200	30p	£2	£8	£16/£30
1843	43 over 34	£2	£8	£30	£60/- - -
1860	160,000	£1	£4	£16	£36/£50
1862	256,000	£1	£3	£12	£25/£40
1862	Proof	(Seaby 1990)	abt.FDC		£475
1870	Proof, or pattern	(1986) - - -		- - -	£325

TWO PENCES
For COPPER TWOPENCES please see page 21

Date	Mintage	Fine	V.F.	E.F.	Unc/FDC abt.

GEORGE III
Silver - 18 mm until 1817

Date	Mintage	Fine	V.F.	E.F.	Unc/FDC abt.
1762		£2	£5	£10	£20/£30
1763		£2	£5	£10	£20/£30
1763	proof	- - -	- - -	- - -	- - -
1765	extremely rare	£100	£250	£600	- - -/- - -
1765	Noted (1991)	(Seaby, nearly E.F. £550)			- - -/- - -
1766		£3	£8	£16	£32/£48
1770		£3	£8	£18	£36/£50
1772	large lettering	£3	£8	£16	£32/£48
1772	small lettering	£3	£8	£16	£32/£48
1780		£2	£6	£12	£25/£40
1784		£3	£8	£16	£32/£48
1786		£3	£8	£16	£32/£48
1792	WIRE MONEY	£7	£16	£32	£50/£85
1795	normal figure 3	£3	£7	£15	£28/- - -
1800		£3	£7	£15	£28/- - -
1817	BULL HEAD 17 mm	30p	£3	£14	£24/£36
1818	17 mm maintained	30p	£3	£15	£25/- - -
1820	17 mm	50p	£3	£14	£22/£36

GEORGE IV
Silver 17 mm

Date	Mintage	Fine	V.F.	E.F.	Unc/FDC abt.
1822	small head	£1	£3	£18	£30/£36
1822	from Maundy proof set		- - -	- - -	
1823	larger normal head	50p	£2	£10	£18/£25
1824		50p	£3	£12	£20/£32
1825		50p	£2	£10	£18/£25
1826		50p	£2	£10	£18/£25
1827		50p	£2	£10	£18/£25
1828		50p	£2	£10	£18/£25
1828	from Maundy proof set		- - -	- - -	- - -/- - -
1829		50p	£2	£10	£18/£25
1830		50p	£2	£10	£18/£25

WILLIAM IV
Silver 17 mm

Date	Mintage	Fine	V.F.	E.F.	Unc/FDC abt.
1831	from Maundy set	50p	£4	£20	£30/£50
1831	from Maundy proof set		- - -	- - -	£36
1832	from Maundy set	50p	£4	£16	£21/£36
1833	from Maundy set	50p	£4	£16	£21/£36

For use in West Indies - unpolished surface:

Date	Mintage	Fine	V.F.	E.F.	Unc/FDC abt.
1834	401,016	£1	£5	£20	£40/£60
1835	491,040	£1	£5	£20	£40/£60
1836	411,840	£1	£4	£18	£36/£55
1837	42,768	£2	£7	£25	£50/£75

Date	Mintage	Fine	V.F.	E.F.	abt. Unc/FDC.
VICTORIA	**Young Head**				
				as Maundy but 'dull' surface	
1838	1,203,840	75p	£4	£20	£40/£60
1838	reads BRITANNIAB (error)	- - -		- - -	
1839	570,240	£2	£5	£30	£60/£90
1840	633,600	£2	£6	£35	£70/£95
1841	443,520	£2	£5	£40	£80/- - -
1842	2,027,520	£2	£5	£40	£80/- - -
1843	Included above	£1	£3	£20	£40/£65
1844	1,045,400	£1	£5	£35	£70/£95
Preceding coins were for use only in the colonies.					
1845	1,314,720	£1	£4	£14	£20/£40
1845	Noted (D.J.Traynor 1990)			BU Gem	£25
1846	47,520	£3	£6	£50	£95/- - -
1849	126,720	£1	£5	£35	£70/£95
1850	950,400	£1	£3	£15	£30/£50
1851	479,065	£1	£3	£25	£50/£75
1853	31,680	£1	£5	£50	£100/- - -
1854	1,467,246	£1	£5	£25	£50/£75
1855	383,350	£1	£5	£40	£80/- - -
1856	1,013,760	£1	£5	£35	£70/- - -
1857	1,758,240	£1	£5	£35	£70/- - -
1858	1,441,440	£1	£5	£35	£70/£95
1858	BRITANNIAB (error)		- -	- - -	- - -/- - -
1859	3,579,840	£1	£3	£10	£20/£35
1860	3,405,600	£1	£4	£20	£40/£60
1861	3,294,720	£1	£3	£15	£30/£45
1862	1,156,320	£1	£4	£25	£45/£65
1863	950,400	£1	£5	£35	£65/- - -
1864	1,330,560	£1	£3	£20	£40/£60
1865	1,742,400	£1	£5	£35	£70/£95
1866	1,900,800	£1	£3	£20	£40/£60
1867	712,800	£1	£4	£25	£50/£75
1868	1,457,280	£1	£3	£20	£40/£60
1868	RRITANNIAR error	£12	£40	£150	- - -/- - -
1868	Laureate Head pattern by Wyon			- - -	- - -/- - -
1869	Colonial only	Noted 1993		- - -	£250
1870	1,283,218	£1	£3	£15	£30/£45
1871	999,633	£1	£3	£20	£40/£50
1872	1,293,271	£1	£3	£15	£30/£45
1873	4,055,550	£1	£2.50	£11	£25/- - -
1874	4,427,031	£1	£2.50	£11	£25/- - -
1875	3,306,500	£1	£2.50	£11	£25/- - -
1876	1,834,389	£1	£2.50	£11	£25/- - -
1877	2,622,393	£1	£2.50	£11	£20/£30
1878	2,419,975	£1	£2.50	£11	£20/£30
1879	3,140,265	£1	£2.50	£11	£20/£30
1880	1,610,069	£1	£3	£15	£25/£40
1881	3,248,265	£1	£3	£15	£22/£40
1882	472,965	£2	£4	£25	£45/£70

See note ★ on page 32

Date	Mintage	Fine	V.F.	E.F.	abt. Unc/FDC

VICTORIA YOUNG HEAD   Silver 16.5 mm

Date	Mintage	Fine	V.F.	E.F.	Unc/FDC
1883	4,365,971	£1	£2	£7	£14/£20
1884	3,322,424	£1	£2	£7	£14/£20
1885	5,183,653	£1	£2	£7	£14/£20
1886	6,152,669	£1	£2	£7	£14/£20
1887	2,780,761 Yg Hd	£1	£3	£15	£30/£45
	Young Head proof	---	---	---	---

JUBILEE HEAD

Date	Mintage	Fine	V.F.	E.F.	Unc/FDC
1887	Included above	50p	£1	£3	£5/£8
1887	Jubilee Head proof	---	---	---	£35/£45
1888	518,199	£1	£2	£8	£15/£25
1889	4,587,010	£1	£2	£6	£12/£20
1890	4,465,834	£1	£2	£6	£12/£20
1891	6,323,027	£1	£2	£4	£8/£12
1892	2,578,226	£1	£2	£6	£12/£20
1893	3,067,243 Jub Hd	£5	£10	£25	£50/£90

OLD or WIDOW HEAD

Date	Mintage	Fine	V.F.	E.F.	Unc/FDC
1893	Included above	60p	£1	£2	£6/£9
	1,312 Proofs	---	---	---	£35/£50
1894	1,608,603	60p	£1	£4	£9/£15
1895	4,788,609	60p	£1	£4	£9/£15
1896	4,598,442	60p	£1	£4	£9/£15
1897	4,541,294	60p	£1	£3	£6/£9
1898	4,567,177	60p	£1	£3	£6/£9
1899	6,246,281	60p	£1	£3	£6/£9
1900	10,644,480	75p	£2	£3	£6/£10
1901	6,098,400	50p	£1	£3	£6/£9

★ Threepences bearing dates not listed are, probably, Maundy pieces.

Date	Mintage	Fine	V.F.	E.F.	Unc/FDC abt.

EDWARD VII

SILVER 16.5mm

Date	Mintage		Fine	V.F.	E.F.	Unc/FDC abt.
1902	8,268,480		65p	£1	£3	£5/£8
1902	15,123	proofs - - -	- - -	- - -		£10/£15
1903	5,227,200		£1	£2	£6	£12/£18
1904	3,627,360		£2	£4	£20	£40/£50
1905	3,548,160		£1	£2	£15	£30/£40
1906	3,152,160		£1	£4	£12	£24/£36
1907	4,831,200		80p	£2	£6	£12/£20
1908	8,157,600		£1	£2	£6	£12/£20
1909	4,055,040		£1	£2	£6	£12/£20
1910	4,563,380		75p	£2	£8	£10/£18

GEORGE V

SILVER (.925 to 1920 then .500) 16.5mm

Date	Mintage		Fine	V.F.	E.F.	Unc/FDC abt.
1911	5,841,084		75p	£2	£3	£6/£10
1911	6,001	proofs - - -	- - -	- - -		£20
1912	8,932,825		60p	£1	£2	£5/£8
1913	7,143,242		60p	£1	£2	£5/£8
1914	6,733,584		60p	£1	£2	£5/£8
1915	5,450,617		60p	£1	£2	£5/£8
1916	18,555,201		60p	£1	£1	£3/£5
1917	21,662,490		60p	£1	£1	£3/£5
1918	20,630,909		60p	£1	£1	£3/£5
1919	16,845,687		60p	£1	£1	£3/£5
1920	16,703,597		50p	75p	£1.50	£4/£6
1920	.500 silver		50p	75p	£1.50	£4/£6
1921	8,749,301		50p	75p	£1.50	£3/£5
1922	7,979,998		50p	75p	£1.50	£3/£5
1923	Small number of patterns, struck in nickel				- -	
1925	3,731,859		£1	£2	£6	£12/£18
1925	Patterns, in nickel, of new (1927) design				- -	- -
1926	4,107,910		£1	£3	£12	£22/£36
1926	Modified Effigy (page 45)		50p	£1.50	£6	£12/£18

> 1904 Large '3' closer to bow at bottom and crown at top.
> 1911 Obv. 1a = neck hollow ⎫ as described on page 11.
>   Obv. 1b = neck flat ⎭

Date	Mintage	Fine	V.F.	E.F.	abt. Unc/FDC

GEORGE V

SILVER (50%) 16.5mm

1927	15,022 proofs oak sprig/acorn reverse			- -	£32/£42
1928	1,302,106	75p	£2	£5	£10/£15
1929	None	- - -	- - -	- - -	- - -/- - -
1930	1,319,412	40p	£1	£4	£8/£12
1931	6,251,936	25p	50p	£1	£2/£4
1932	5,887,325	25p	50p	£1	£2/£4
1933	5,578,541	25p	50p	£1	£2/£4
1934	7,405,954	25p	50p	£1	£2/£4
1934	A proof offered for sale in 1976 (!)				/£55
1935	7,027,654	12p	25p	£1	£2/£3
1936	3,238,670	10p	20p	£1	£2/£3

EDWARD VIII   (Duke of Windsor)
A PATTERN BEARING A DESIGN OF THREE RINGS   Page 49

GEORGE VI

SILVER (50%) 16.5mm

1937	8,148,156	25p	50p	70p	£1.50/£2
1937	26,402 proofs	- - -	- - -	- - -	£3/£5
1938	6,402,473	- - -	25p	50p	£1/£2
1939	1,355,860	25p	50p	£1	£3/£5
1940	7,914,401	20p	45p	60p	£1.50/£2
1941	7,979,411	25p	50p	£1	£2/£3
1942	4,144,051 Colonial	£1	£2	£5	£9/£15
1943	1,379,220 Colonial	£1	£3	£6	£10/£16
1944	2,005,553 Colonial	£2	£5	£10	£15/£20
1945	371,000 dated 1944; re-melted by The Mint				
	One dated 1945 is known to have 'escaped'.				

Date	Mintage		Fine	V.F.	E.F.	Unc/abt FDC

EDWARD VIII Duke of Windsor DODECAGONAL

1937	Date divided by THRIFT PLANT (Sea-pink); a few were made for slot machine testing and thicknesses vary. Spinks (1990) £28.500	
1937	Date at bottom, but effigy Edward VIII. Certainly rarer than that listed above. Lettering is EDWARDVS VIII *not* GEORGIVS VI.	

GEORGE VI DODECAGONAL - MODIFIED THRIFT PLANT

Date	Mintage		Fine	V.F.	E.F.	Unc/abt FDC
1937	45,707,957		- - -	15p	50p	£1/£2
1937	26,402	proofs	- - -	- -		£4
1938	14,532,332		5p	30p	£3	£5/£8
1939	5,603,021		12p	60p	£4	£15/£20
1940	12,636,018		10p	50p	£2	£3/£4
1941	60,239,489		- - -	15p	£1	£2/£3
1942	103,214,400		- - -	12p	£1	£2/£3
1943	101,702,400		- - -	12p	50p	£1/£2
1944	69,760,000		- - -	15p	50p	£1/£3
1945	33,942,466		- - -	20p	£1.25	£3/£6
1946	620,734		£1	£5	£30	£125/£155
1946	Proof		- - -	- - -	- - -	FDC £250
1946	Proof	Noted 1991 (Coincraft)			£195	- - - -
1947	None		- - -	- - -	- - -	- - -
1948	4,230,400		12p	£1	£3	£6/£10

IND. IMP discontinued

1948	Proof	Noted 1991 (Coincraft)			- - -	£295
1949	464,000		£1	£5	£30	£60/£90
1949	A proof in brass		- - -	- - -	- - -	£200
1950 } *	1,600,000		10p	£1	£8	£20/£40
1950 }	17,513	proofs	- - -	- - -	- - -	£10/£15
1951	1,184,000		10p	£1	£8	£20/£40
1951	20,000	proofs	- - -	- - -	- - -	£20
1952	25,494,400		- - -	20p	£1	£2/£3
	British Museum has proof/s of each date					

1937	Two different spacings from rim of word THREE noted : Rev. A = large gap; Rev. B = small gap

★ A "Strange Madness" when a superb proof striking costs less than one struck for general circulation.

Sharp v Rounded Corners:
1937 - 1940 All sharp
1941 - Both
1942 - 1946 All rounded
1948 - Both
1949 - All rounded
1950 - 1952 All sharp

DODECAGONAL

Date	Mintage	Fine	V.F.	E.F.	abt. Unc/ FDC

ELIZABETH II   PORTCULLIS with CHAINS, ROYALLY CROWNED

Date	Mintage	Fine	V.F.	E.F.	abt. Unc/ FDC
1953	30,618,000	BRITT.OMN	25p	50p	75p/£1.50
1953	40,000	proofs Obv.2	- - -	- - -	£2/£4
1954	41,720,000	no BRITT.OMN	25p	50p	£1/£3
1954	Matt proof	(1982 - Seaby)			£90
1955	41,075,200	- - -	25p	50p	£1/£2
1956	36,801,600	- - -	45p	£1	£2/£4
1957	24,294,400	- - -	25p	50p	£1/£3
1958	20,504,000	- - -	45p	£1	£4/£8
1958	Proof	(Coincraft 1993)		FDC	£275
1959	28,499,200	- - -	- - -	50p	£2/£3
1960	83,078,400	- - -	- - -	25p	£1/£2
1961	41,102,400	- - -	- - -	10p	40p/95p
1962	51,545,600	- - -	- - -	10p	30p/90p
1963	35,280,000	- - -	- - -	10p	20p/80p
1964	44,867,200	- - -	- - -	5p	10p/40p
1965	27,160,000	- - -	- - -	5p	10p/40p
1966	53,760,000	- - -	- - -	- - -	10p/40p
1967	151,780,800	- - -	- - -	- - -	5p/20p
1970	750,476	proofs for LAST STERLING set			- - -/ - - -

V.A.T., not included here, is sometimes
absorbed by the seller on a 'special offer' basis.

1953	(a) = I of ELIZABETH points to corner of rim/edge. (b) = I is much further to the right (see page 65).
1953	Obv. 1 Details, particularly head ribbon and initials M.G. are poorly defined = ex-specimen set (page 95).
	Obv. 2 Portrait more sharply outlined as are the ends of the head ribbon = normal issue. Both have ovoid stops.
1954	Much sharper overall and with round stops.

Date	Mintage	Fine	V.F.	E.F.	abt. Unc./FDC
GEORGE III	Reverse has LARGE FIGURE 4 · SILVER 19.5mm				
1763	Young Armoured Bust	£2	£7	£16	- - - / - - -
1763	Extremely rare proof	- - -	- - -	- - -	- - - / - - -
1765	Extremely rare currency	£100	£200	£500	- - - / - - -
1766		£4	£8	£16	- - - / - - -
1770		£4	£8	£16	- - - / - - -
1772		£4	£8	£16	- - - / - - -
1772	2 struck over 0	£4	£16	£32	- - - / - - -
1776		£3	£6	£12	- - - / - - -
1780		£3	£6	£12	- - - / - - -
1784		£4	£8	£16	- - - / - - -
1786		£4	£8	£16	- - - / - - -
1792	Thin 4 (wire money)	£6	£12	£24	- - - / - - -
1794	Normal 4 from Maundy	£3	£8	£16	- - - / - - -
1800	Also from Maundy	£3	£6	£12	- - - / - - -
WILLIAM IV	Reverse has FOUR PENCE in words - SILVER 16.5mm				
1836	Britannia seated	£1	£2	£10	£20 / £30
1836	Proofs, grained in silver	- -	- - -	- - -	- - - / - - -
1836	Proofs, plain edge in gold	- -	- - -	- - -	- - - / - - -
1836	Proofs, plain edge in silver		£275	£350	- - - / - - -
1837	962,280	£1	£2	£10	£20 / £30

A number of patterns exist

The FOURPENCE, not the silver threepence, is the true "Joey": taking its name from one Joseph Hume who recommended it to facilitate payment of the, then, 4d London omnibus fare.

Date	Mintage	Fine	V.F.	E.F.	abt. Unc/FDC
VICTORIA		FOUR PENCE in words - SILVER 16.5mm			
1837	Proof only - plain edged		- - -		- - -
1837	Proof only - grained (milled) edge			- - -	
1838	2,150,280	£1	£3	£12	£28/£40
1838	2nd 8 struck over ∞	£1	£3	£20	£45/£65
1838	Plain edged proof	- - -	- - -	- - -	£120
1839	1,461,240	£1	£3	£12	£24/£35
1839	Plain edged proof from the sets			- - -	£130
1840	1,496,880	£1	£3	£10	£20/£30
1841	344,520	£2	£7	£25	£48/£75
1842	724,680	£1	£3	£12	£36/£50
1842	Plain edged proof	- - -	- - -	- - -	£130
1842	2 struck over 1	£3	£8	£50	- - -
1843	1,817,640	£1	£3	£18	£36/£54
1844	855,360	£1	£4	£20	£48/£68
1845	914,760	£1	£4	£20	£45/£65
1846	1,366,200	60p	£3	£16	£32/£50
1847	7 struck over 6	£15	£32	£95	£120/£175
1848	712,800	£3	£6	£16	£36/- - -
1848	2nd 8 over 6	£2	£5	£20	£45/£65
1848	2nd 8 over 7	£2	£5	£20	£45/£65
1849	380,160	£1	£4	£19	£40/- - -
1849	9 struck over 8	£2	£7	£30	£60/£80
1851	594,000	£12	£50	£140	£180/£250
1852	31,300	£25	£80	£200	£350/- - - -
1853	11,880	£30	£90	£250	£450/- - - -
1853	Grained (milled) edge proof from set			- - -	£300
1853	Plain edged proof	- - -	- - -	£150	- - - -
1854	1,096,613	£1	£3	£15	£25/£36
1854	5 struck over 3	£1	£3	£18	£36/- - -
1855	646,041	£1	£3	£16	£32/- - -
1857	Proof only, grained edge		- - -	- - -	£650
1862	Proof only, plain edge		- - -	- - -	£450
1888	JUBILEE HEAD (Br.Guiana)	£8	£20	£30/£50	
1888	Grained edge proof	- - -	- - -	- - -	- - -

1840   narrow 'O'   not seen
1841   4I instead of 41   not seen

Date	Mintage/etc	Fine	V.F.	E.F.	Unc/abt FDC
GEORGE III	ARMOURED BUST to 1816				SILVER 21/22mm
1786	Pattern - no hearts in Shield of Hanover			- - -	
1787	No hearts illustrations	£3	£7	£11	£16/£25
1787	With hearts page 57	£3	£7	£11	£16/£25
1787	Proof, without hearts	- - -	- - -	- - -	£275
1788	Pattern by Droz (ESC 1642)		- - -	£300	- - - -
1790	Pattern by Droz (ESC 1645)		- - -	£250	- - - -
1790	Pattern by Droz (ESC 1646)		- - -	£150	- - - -
1791	Pattern by Droz (ESC 1647)		- - -	£300	- - - -
	BULL HEAD				SILVER 19 mm
1816	Included below	£1.50	£5	£12	£24/£36
1816	Proof in gold	- - -	- - -	- - -	- - - -
1817	10,921,680 (inc 1816)	£3	£6	£15	£30/£45
1817	Proof, plain edge	- - -	- - -	(1985)	£300
1818	4,284,720	£3	£8	£25	£50/£80
1819	4,712,400	£2	£6	£20	£30/£50
1819	Very small 8	£4	£9	£36	£75/- - -
1820	1,448,960	£2	£6	£25	£36/£55
1820	Inverted 1 ‡820	£15	£45	£150	£240/- - -
GEORGE IV					SILVER 19mm
1820	Proof only, garnished shield		- - -		£600/£750
1821	863,280	£3	£14	£30	£60/£100
1821	Proof (ESC 1655) - - -		- - -	- - -	£350/- - - -
1821	BBITANNIAR error	£30	£60	£120	£240/£360
1824	633,600 garter	£3	£14	£50	£110/£160
1825	483,120 garter	£3	£14	£50	£110/£160
1825	Pattern for BARE HEAD design (Spink)		- - -		£2,000
1826	689,040	£8	£35	£125	£250/£325
1826	A proof - Shield within garter - - -				£125
Type change to BARE HEAD - LION on CROWN reverse					
1826	Included above	£2	£8	£36	£50/£75
1826	A proof - Bare Head/Lion on Crown				£125/£200
1827	166,320	£6	£30	£80	£165/£220
1828	15,840 ?	£4	£24	£65	£125/- - - -
1829	403,920	£3	£15	£60	£100/- - - -
WILLIAM IV					SILVER 19mm
1831	1,340,195	£2	£10	£30	£65/£95
1831	A proof - plain edge	- - -	- - -	- - -	£75/£95
1834	5,892,480	£2	£10	£40	£90/£130
1835	1,552,320	£2	£10	£40	£90/£130
1836	1,987,920	£5	£20	£85	£120/- - - -
1837	506,880	£3	£16	£60	£100/£150

Date	Mintage/etc	Fine	V.F.	E.F.	abt. Unc/FDC
VICTORIA		**Young Head**			SILVER 19mm
1838	1,607,760	£2	£8	£40	£75/£110
1839	3,310,560	£2	£7	£35	£70/£100
1839	A proof or pattern	- - -	- - -	- - -	£145/£160
1840	2,098,800	£3	£9	£38	£75/£110
1840	Pattern by W.Wyon rev cancelled with fine lines				- - - / - - -
1841	1,386,000	£3	£14	£45	£75/ - - -
1841	Pattern, gold, using half-sovereign reverse				
1842	601,920	£3	£12	£45	£90/£130
1843	3,160,080	£2	£10	£40	£80/£120
1844	3,975,840	£2	£9	£32	£70/ - - -
1844	Has large 44	£3	£12	£42	£90/ - - -
1845	3,714,480	£2	£10	£40	£80/£120
1846	4,268,880	£2	£10	£35	£60/£85
1847	Would seem to exist	- - -	- - -	- - -	- - - / - - -
1848	586,080	£12	£50	£130	£250/ - - -
1848	8 struck over 6	- - -	£60	£145	£250/ - - -
1848	8 struck over 7	- - -	£60	£145	£250/ - - -
1850	498,960	£3	£10	£45	£100/ - - -
1850	5 struck over 3	- - -	(Cooke 1990 abt.BU £99)		
1851	2,288,107	£2	£9	£36	£75/£120
1852	904,586	£2	£9	£36	£75/£120
1853	3,837,930	£2	£8	£25	£40/£70
1853	A proof	- - -	- - -	- - -	£300
1854	840,116	£25	£85	£300	- - - -
1855	1,129,084	£2	£9	£32	£65/£95
1855	A proof	- - -	- - -	- - -	£250
1856	2,779,920	£2	£9	£32	£65/£95
1856	A pattern worded	HALF	SHILLING		- - - -
1856	A pattern worded	1/2	SHILLING		- - - -
1857	2,233,440	£2	£9	£32	£65/£95
1858	1,932,480	£2	£9	£32	£65/£95
1858	A Proof	- - -	- - -	- - -	£250
1859	4,688,640	£2	£9	£30	£60/£90
1859	9 struck over 8	(Spink 1988 GEF £145)			
1860	1,100,880	£2	£9	£35	£75/£120
1862	990,000	£10	£35	£115	£250/ - - -
1863	491,040	£6	£25	£85	£150/ - - -

NOW WITH DIE NUMBER (above date, below wreath)

1864	4,253,040	£2	£9	£40	£65/£95
1865	1,631,520	£2	£12	£45	£75/ - - -
1866	5,140,080	£2	£9	£40	£70/£105
1866	No die number	£18	£65	£200	- - - -
1867	1,362,240	£3	£16	£50	£95/ - - -
1867	A proof	- - -	- - -	- - -	£250
1868	1,069,200	£3	£16	£50	£95/ - - -
1869	388,080	£3	£17	£52	£95/£145
1869	A proof	- - -	- - -	- - -	£180/ - - - -
1856	Variety: longer line below PENCE - rare				
1857	Variety: longer line below PENCE - rare				

Date	Mintage	Fine	V.F.	E.F.	Unc/abt FDC
VICTORIA (continued)		*DIE NUMBER above date, below wreath*			
1870	479,613	£4	£15	£60	£90/£145
1870	A proof	---	---	---	£155
1871	3,662,684	£2	£8	£25	£50/£80
1871	A proof	---	---	---	£160
1871	No die number	£3	£12	£50	£75/---
1871	A proof without die number		---	---	£225
1872	3,382,048 die no.	£2	£8	£20	£40/£60
1873	4,594,733 die no.	£2	£8	£20	£40/£60
1874	4,225,726 die no.	£2	£8	£20	£40/£60
1875	3,256,545 die no.	£2	£8	£20	£40/£60
1876	841,435 die no.	£4	£12	£50	£75/£112
1877	4,066,486 die no.	£2	£8	£20	£40/---
1877	No die number	£2	£8	£25	£45/---
1878	2,624,525 die no.	£2	£8	£20	£40/---
1878	A proof of previous coin	---	---	---	£155
1878	8 struck over 7	---	---	----	----
1878	DRITANNIAR error	£15	£45	£200	£375
1879	3,326,313	£4	£12	£40	£65/£100
	DIE NUMBERS DISCONTINUED				
1879	Included above	£2	£9	£25	£50/---
1879	A proof	---	---	---	£125
1880	Hair lock on cheek	£3	£10	£30	£60/---
1880	No lock of hair ★	£2	£6	£15	£30/£50
1880	No lock of hair ★ ★	(Colin Cooke 1991) abt. BU	---	/£50	
	★ ★ The reverse of this example has smaller lettering than ★				
1880	A proof	---	---	---	£125
1881	6,239,447	£2	£6	£20	£40/£65
1881	A proof	---	---	---	£150
1882	759,809	£3	£12	£36	£72/---
1883	4,986,558	£2	£6	£12	£25/£40
1884	3,422,565	£2	£6	£15	£25/£40
1884	Pattern bearing national emblems	---	---	---	£300
1885	4,652,771	£2	£6	£9	£15/£25
1886	2,728,249	£2	£6	£10	£20/£40
1886	A proof	---	---	---	£125
1887	3,675,607 Young Head	£2	£5	£10	£20/£30
1887	A proof Young Head	---	---	---	£120

First Young Head 1838 to 1866 inclusive.
Second Young Head 1867 to 1880; as first but lower relief.
* Third Young Head 1880 to 1887; no hairlock: Rev has larger lettering.

"Gothic" Head

Young Head

Jubilee Head

"Bun" Head

Old, Veiled,
or Widow Head

GILLICK
(Mary Gillick)

MACHIN
(Arnold Machin)

MAKLOUF
(Raphael Maklouf)

Date	Mintage	Fine	V.F.	E.F.	Unc/abt. FDC

VICTORIA   Jubilee Head

Reverse --A-- *GARTERED SHIELD 'WITHDRAWN':*

| 1887 | 3,675,607 | £1 | £2 | £3 | £5/£8 |
| 1887 | Proof Gartered Shield | -- | --- | | £50/£75 |

Being the same size and design as the half-sovereign many were gold plated and passed as such. This led to the withdrawal of this design of sixpence.

| 1887 | Pattern - Gartered Shield - date above crown | | | | |

Reverse --B-- *CROWNED VALUE IN WREATH:*

1887	Included above	£1	£2	£4	£6/£9
1887	Proof Crowned Value In Wreath	---	---		£50/£75
1887	Patterns by Spink, Lion- Shield- Unicorn Reverse:				
	in gold, brass, copper, tin and aluminium.				
1888	4,197,698	£1	£3	£6	£12/£18
1888	A proof	---	---	---	£115
1889	8,738,928	£1	£3	£10	£20/£30
1890	9,386,955	£1	£4	£14	£28/£42
1890	A proof	---	---	---	£115
1891	7,022,734	£1	£3	£12	£24/£30
1892	6,245,746	£1	£3	£10	£20/£30
1893	7,350,619 Jubilee Head	£65	£175	£500	£750/£1200

OLD or WIDOW HEAD

1893	Included above	£1	£2	£9	£18/£25
1893	A proof	---	---	£25	£40/£60
1894	3,467,704	£1	£3	£12	£22/£34
1895	7,024,631	£1	£3	£9	£18/£26
1896	6,651,699	£1	£3	£9	£18/£26
1897	5,031,498	£1	£3	£9	£18/£26
1898	5,914,100	£1	£3	£10	£20/£30
1899	7,996,804	£1	£3	£9	£18/£26
1900	8,984,354	£1	£3	£7	£14/£21
1901	5,108,757	£1	£3	£7	£14/£21

The sixpence became known as a "TANNER". The cab fare from the City of London to Tanner's Hill cost sixpence i.e. "A Tanner One".

--A--   --B--

Date	Mintage	Fine	V.F.	E.F.	abt. Unc/FDC

EDWARD VII   CROWNED SIXPENCE WITHIN WREATH 19mm

1902	6,367,378	£1	£2	£8	£10/£18
1902	15,123 proofs with matt finish	- -	- - -		FDC £12
1903	5,410,096	£1	£5	£15	£40/£60
1904	4,487,098	£2	£8	£25	£60/£85
1904	noted		(Spink 1989 toned UNC £60)		
1905	4,235,556	£2	£8	£22	£50/£70
1906	7,641,146	£1	£3	£14	£30/£40
1907	8,733,673	£1	£4	£16	£30/£45
1908	6,739,491	£1	£7	£21	£45/£65
1909	6,584,017	£1	£4	£15	£35/£50
1910	12,490,724	£1	£3	£9	£12/£25

GEORGE V   LION ON CROWN   19mm

1911	9,155,310	- - -	£1.50	£5	£9/£15
1911	6,007 proofs	- - -	- - -	- - -	£22/£30
1912	10,984,129	- - -	£2	£12	£24/£36
1913	7,499,833	- - -	£3	£12	£24/£36
1914	22,714,602	- - -	£1	£5	£9/£15
1915	15,694,597	- - -	£1	£5	£9/£15
1916	22,207,178	- - -	£1	£5	£9/£15
1917	7,725,475	- - -	£2	£12	£24/£36
1918	27,558,743	- - -	£1	£6	£10/£15
1919	13,375,447	- - -	£1	£8	£18/£25
1920	14,136,287:				
	Silver .925	- - -	£2	£9	£18/- - -
	Silver .500	- - -	£1.50	£8	£15/£24
1921	30,339,741	- - -	£1	£6	£12/£24
1922	16,878,890	- - -	£1	£7	£15/£24
1923	6,382,793	- - -	£3	£12	£20/£30
1924	17,444,218	- - -	£1	£5	£10/£15
1925	12,720,558	- - -	£1	£5	£10/£15
1925	With new broader rim	- - -	£1.50	£9	£12/£20
1925	A pattern of the 1928 design in nickel				- - -
1926	21,809,261	- - -	£1	£9	£16/£25
1926	Modified Effigy (page 45)	£1	£3	£6	£10/£16
1927	68,939,873	£1	£2	£5	£9/£15
1927	15,000 proofs - Rev. new OAK/ACORN design				£12
1928	23,123,384	- - -	50p	£3	£5/£8
1929	28,319,326	- - -	50p	£3	£5/£9
1930	16,990,289	- - -	60p	£3	£7/£10
1931	16,873,268 ★	- - -	75p	£5'	£8/£12
1931	A proof	- - -	- - -	- - -	£175
1932	9,406,127 ★	- - -	75p	£4	£8/£14
1933	22,185,083	- - -	50p	£3	£5/£8
1933	A proof	- - -	- - -	- - -	£180
1934	9,304,009	- - -	60p	£4	£7/£12
1935	13,995,621	- - -	50p	£3	£6/£8
1936	24,380,171	- - -	30p	£2	£4/£6

★ these have a finer grained (milled) edge

EDWARD VIII   (Duke of Windsor)

1937	SIX LINKED RINGS of ST.EDWARD		page 49 £9,500

MODIFIED EFFIGY: in the absence of a direct comparison, the modified effigy (or modified head) can be distinguished by the initials which appear on the truncation of the neck. Before modification, the initials B.M. are placed near the centre of truncation. After modification they appear, without stops, well to the right thus : BM (not B.M.) - Bertram Mackennal - designer of the coin.

Date	Mintage	Fine	V.F.	E.F.	abt. Unc/FDC
GEORGE VI		*50% SILVER, 50% ALLOY to 1946 - 19mm*			
1937	22,302,524	- - -.	25p	£1.50	£2.50/£4
1937	26,402 proofs	- - -	- - -	- - -	£3/£5
1938	13,402,701	- - -	- - -	£3	£6/£9
1939	28,670,304	- - -	- - -	£1.50	£3/£4
1940	20,875,196	- - -	- - -	£1.50	£3/£4
1941	23,186,616	- - -	- - -	£1.50	£3/£4
1942	44,942,785	- - -	- - -	£1	£3/£4
1943	46,927,111	- - -	- - -	£1	£3/£4
1944	37,952,600	- - -	- - -	£1	£2/£3
1945	39,939,259	- - -	- - -	£1	£2/£3
1946	43,466,407	- - -	- - -	£1	£2/£3
	CUPRO-NICKEL				
1946	Proof, for new coinage, in cupro-nickel			- - -	- - -
1947	29,993,263	- - -	- - -	45p	£1/£2
1948	88,323,540	- - -	- - -	65p	£1/£3
Monogram GRI was changed to GRVI in 1949 when title IND:					
IMP: (INDAE IMPERATOR) - Emperor of India- was relinquished					
1949	41,355,515	- - -	- - -	75p	£2/£4
1950	32,741,955	- - -	- - -	65p	£2/£3
1950	17,513 proofs	- - -	- - -	- - -	£3/£5
1951	40,399,491	- - -	- - -	65p	£2/£3
1951	20,000 proofs	- - -	- - -	- - -	£3/£5
1952	1,013,477	50p	£1.50	£10	£20/£30
ELIZABETH II		NATIONAL EMBLEMS INTERTWINED			
1953	70,323,876	- - -	- - -	25p	50p/75p
1953	40,000 proofs	- - -	- - -	- - -	£2/£4
	BRITT: OMN: discontinued				
1954	105,241,150	- - -	- - -	35p	£2/£3
1955	109,929,554	- - -	- - -	20p	50p/£1
1956	109,841,555	- - -	- - -	20p	50p/£1
1957	105,654,290	- - -	- - -	18p	30p/50p
1958	123,518,527	- - -	- - -	65p	£2/£3
1959	93,089,441	- - -	- - -	- - -	20p/45p
1960	103,288,346	- - -	- - -	50p	£1/£2
1961	115,052,017	- - -	- - -	50p	£1/£2
1962	178,359,637	- - -	- - -	- - -	30p/60p
1963	112,964,000	- - -	- - -	- - -	20p/45p
1964	152,336,000	- - -	- - -	- - -	20p/45p
1965	129,644,000	- - -	- - -	- - -	15p/30p
1966	175,696,000	- - -	- - -	- - -	10p/20p
1966	"Mule" with Commonwealth Portrait @ auction 1993				£396
1967	240,788,000	- - -	- - -	- - -	15p
1970	750,476 proofs for LAST STERLING set			- - -	£1

Various 'pointings' have been noted (see page 65)

1953 ELIZABETH; ELIZABETH.

1955 SIXPENCE; SIXPENCE.

1964 and 1965 REGINA; REGINA.

EIGHTPENCES and OCTORINOS

abt.
Unc/FDC

GEORGE V		ESC refers to Seaby's "The English Silver Coinage"		
PATTERNS by HUTH		Central Star bears LEGS OF MAN		
1913	ESC 1481A	Pattern for eightpence in copper		---
	ESC 1481	OCTORINO	--- ---	£300/----
	ESC 1481	Noted (Seaby 1990) abt.FDC		£450
1913	ESC 1482	EIGHTPENCE in silver	---	----/£450
	ESC 1482A	EIGHT PENCE in copper	---	----
		(Spink 1980) in iron		£225/----

These items appear only very rarely.

1913
OCTORINO

Date		V.F.	E.F.	abt. Unc./FDC

GEORGE III Bank Token   Silver 22mm

1812   Pattern bank token.
     Rev has BANK TOKEN 9D and the date in wreath of Oak and Olive:

	(ESC 1478)	- - -	£150	£375 £600/£850
1812	As above (ESC 1479) in copper	- - -	£400	£650/£900
1812	As above (ESC 1480) silver 9 PENCE	- - -		£700/£950

TENPENCES

VICTORIA One Franc   Silver 23mm

1867   Pattern - ESC 1416 ONE FRANC/TEN PENCE   £350   £700/£950

The Coinage of EDWARD VIII (Duke of Windsor)

OBVERSE: coins in silver.

OBVERSE: coins in bronze, nickel-brass, and gold.

Briefly: specially struck silver coins are distributed to as many old men and women as the Monarch has years; those years being 'expressed' in pence. Thus, on the Monarch's fortieth birthday, 40 men and 40 women each receive 40 pence or four Maundy sets at tenpence per set. The following year the distribution would be to 41 men and 41 women: four sets plus an extra penny. There are additonal sums, paid in conventional notes and coins, in lieu of food and clothing. The distribution takes place on Maundy Thursday: the day before Good Friday.

SILVER

MAUNDY SETS

FACE VALUE TEN PENCE   THE SET OF FOUR COINS

Date		Fine	V.F.	abt. E.F./Unc.
GEORGE III				
1763		£25	£50	£100/£150
1763	A proof set of utmost rarity		- - -	- - -
1765	Rarity equals that of 1763 proof			- - -
1766		£25	£50	£100/£150
1772	noted (2d 7 over 6; 4d 2 over 0)		abt.EF £100	
1780		£25	£50	£100/£150
1784		£25	£50	£100/£150
1786	(Seaby 1988)	GVF	£60	- - -
1792	★ WIRE MONEY	£55	£100	£150/£250
1795	Return to normal numbering	£20	£30	£60/£90
1800		£20	£30	£60/£90
1817	'NEW' COINAGE • BULL HEAD	£40		£80/£120
1818		- - -	£40	£80/£120
1820		- - -	£40	£80/£120

     ★ WIRE MONEY is so called because of the thin, 'wiry' script used for the figures   1, 2, 3, 4.

		V.F.	E.F.	abt. Unc./FDC
GEORGE IV				
1822		£30	£60	£90/£120
1822	A proof set (ESC 2426)	- - -	- - -	£150
1823		£25	£50	£75/£100
1824		£30	£80	£125/£140
1825	to 1828	£25	£50	£75/£100
1828	A proof set (ESC 2433)	- - -	- - -	£150
1829		£25	£50	£75/£100
1830		£25	£50	£75/£100
1830	noted	(Saltford Coins 1989 choice FDC £98)		

M A U N D Y   O D D M E N T S :

		V.F.	E.F.	Abt. Unc/FDC			V.F.	E.F.	Abt. Unc/FDC
1762	3d	£5	£10	- - -/- - -	1792	1d	- - -	£9	- - -/- - -
1765	2d	£225	- - -	- - -/- - -	1792	2d	£12	£25	- - -/- - -
1765	3d	- - -	£600	- - -/- - -	1792	3d	£15	£30	- - -/- - -
1779	1d	- - -	£25	- - -/- - -	1792	4d	£15	£30	- - -/- - -
1781	1d	- - -	£25	- - -/- - -	1800	2d	- - -	£5	- - -/- - -
1784	1d	- - -	£8	- - -/- - -	1818	1d	- - -	- - -	- - -/£15
					1829	1d	- - -	£6	£9/- - -

(Above) 1792 "WIRE MONEY"

WILLIAM IV   Silver as illustrated

Date	VF.	EF.	abt. FDC from/to	Date	VF.	EF.	abt. FDC from/to
1831	£35	£80	£130/£200	1834	£35	£80	£130/£200
1831	Proof		£100/£250	1835	£35	£80	£120/£150
1831	Proof in gold		- - - -	1836	£35	£80	£120/£150
1832	£35	£80	£120/£150	1837	£35	£80	£120/£150
1833	£35	£80	£120/£150				

VICTORIA   *Young Head*

Date	Sets	EF.	abt Unc/FDC	Date	Sets	EF.	abt Unc/FDC
1838	4,158	£35	£50/£65	1871	4,488	£36	£50/£65
1838	Proofs	- - -	£115	1871	Proof Auct.89		£410
1838	Proofs in gold	- - -		1872	4,328	£36	£50/£65
1839	4,125	£35	£50/£70	1873	4,162	£36	£50/£65
1839	Proofs	- - -	£185	1874	4,488	£36	£50/£65
1840	4,125	£35	£50/£65	1875	4,154	£36	£50/£65
1841	2,574	£35	£50/£65	1876	4,488	£36	£50/£65
1842	4,125	£35	£50/£65	1877	4,488	£36	£50/£65
1843	4,158	£35	£50/£65	1878	4,488	£36	£50/£65
1844	4,158	£35	£50/£65	1878	Proofs	- - -	£200
1845	4,158	£35	£50/£65	1879	4,488	£36	£50/£65
1846	4,158	£35	£50/£65	1880	4,488	£36	£50/£65
1847	4,158	£35	£50/£65	1881	Proofs	- - -	£200
1848	4,158	£35	£50/£65	1882	4,488	£36	£50/£65
1849	4,158	£42	£60/£75	1883	4,488	£36	£50/£65
1850	4,158	£35	£55/£70	1884	4,488	£36	£50/£65
1851	4,158	£35	£55/£70	1885	4,488	£36	£50/£65
1852	4,158	£35	£55/£70	1886	4,488	£36	£50/£65
1853	4,158	£35	£55/£70	1887	4,488	£40	£55/£75
1853	Proofs	- - -	£350/£500				
1854	4,158	£36	£50/£65			*Jubilee Head*	
1855	4,158	£36	£50/£65	1888	4,488	£36	£50/£65
1856	4,158	£36	£50/£65	1888	Proofs	- - -	- - -
1857	4,158	£36	£50/£65	1889	4,488	£45	£55/£70
1858	4,158	£36	£50/£65	1890	4,488	£45	£55/£70
1859	4,158	£36	£50/£65	1891	4,488	£45	£55/£70
1860	4,158	£36	£50/£65	1892	4,488	£45	£55/£70
1861	4,158	£36	£50/£65				
1862	4,158	£36	£50/£65			*Old or Widow Head*	
1863	4,158	£36	£50/£65	1893	8,976	£25	£35/£45
1864	4,158	£36	£50/£65	1894	8,976	£25	£35/£45
1865	4,158	£36	£50/£65	1895	8,877	£25	£35/£45
1867	4,158	£36	£50/£65	1896	8,476	£25	£35/£45
1867	Proofs		£265	1897	8,976	£25	£35/£45
1868	4,158	£36	£50/£65	1898	8,976	£25	£35/£45
1869	4,158	£36	£50/£65	1899	8,976	£25	£35/£45
1870	4,488	£36	£50/£65	1900	8,976	£25	£35/£45
				1901	8,976	£25	£35/£45

Original Documentation Adds Value/add £5 for dated case of issue

EDWARD VII

Date	Sets	EF.	F.D.C. from/to	Date	Sets	EF.	F.D.C. from/to
1902	8,976	£30	£40/£50	1906	8,800	£25	£35/£40
1902	15,123	matt proofs £40		1907	8,760	£25	£35/£40
1903	8,976	£25	£35/£40	1908	8,760	£25	£35/£40
1904	8,876	£25	£35/£40	1909	1,983	£35	£45/£55
1905	8,976	£25	£35/£40	1910	1,440	£40	£50/£60

GEORGE V

Date	Sets	EF.	Unc/FDC	Date	Sets	EF.	Unc/FDC
1911	1,768	£30	£40/£45	1924	1,515	£25	£35/£45
1911	proofs	- - -	£60	1925	1,438	£25	£35/£45
1912	1,246	£25	£35/£40	1926	1,504	£25	£35/£45
1913	1,228	£25	£35/£40	1927	1,647	£25	£35/£45
1914	982	£42	£50/£60	1928	1,642	£25	£35/£45
1915	1,293	£25	£35/£40	1929	1,761	£25	£35/£45
1916	1,128	£25	£35/£40	1930	1,724	£25	£35/£45
1917	1,237	£25	£35/£40	1931	1,759	£25	£35/£45
1918	1,375	£25	£35/£40	1932	1,835	£25	£35/£45
1919	1,258	£25	£35/£40	1933	1,872	£25	£35/£45
1920	1,399	£25	£35/£40	1934	1,887	£25	£35/£45
1921	1,386	£25	£35/£40	1935	1,928	£30	£45/£55
1922	1,373	£25	£35/£40	1936	1,323	£35	£50/£60
1923	1,430	£40	£45/£55		Orig. Documents Add Value		

MAUNDY ODDMENTS (Virtually Mintlike)

	1d	2d	3d	4d		1d	2d	3d	4d
1822	£9	- -	- -	- -	1898	- -	- -	- -	£7
1850	£6	- -	- -	£6	1900	- -	£4	- -	- -
1870	£5	- -	- -	- -	1902	- -	£4	£12	- -
1880	£5	- -	- -	- -	1904	£5	£5	£9	£6
1888	£5	- -	- -	- -	1911	- -	- -	- -	£6

GEORGE VI

Date	Sets	abt Unc/FDC	Date	Sets	abt Unc/FDC
1937	1,325	£30/£40	1945	1,355	£30/£40
1938	1,275	£30/£40	1946	1,365	£30/£40
1939	1,234	£30/£40	1947	1,375	£30/£40
1940	1,277	£30/£40	1948	1,385	£30/£40
1941	1,253	£30/£40	1949	1,395	£30/£40
1942	1,231	£30/£40	1950	1,405	£30/£40
1943	1,239	£30/£40	1951	1,468	£30/£40
1944	1,259	£30/£40	1952	1,012	£30/£40

> 1937 to 1946 .500 silver was used.
> 1947 to 1952 a return to Sterling silver
> 1949 to 1952 a change of inscription
> 1952 Maundy was distributed by Queen Elizabeth.
> 1954 to 1970 a change of inscription.
> 1971 change to decimal.

Date	Complete Sets		Unc/FDC

ELIZABETH II

Date	Complete Sets		Unc/FDC
1953	1,025	St.Paul's Cathedral	£195/£225
1953	In gold	- - - (1985)	£5,750
1954	1,020	Westminster Abbey	£35/£45
1955	1,036	Southwark Cathedral	£35/£45
1956	1,088	Westminster Abbey	£35/£45
1957	1,094	St.Alban's Cathedral	£35/£45

Date   Complete Sets

ELIZABETH II

Unc./ FDC

Date	Complete Sets			Unc./ FDC
1958	1,100	Westminster Abbey		£40/£50
1959	1,106	Windsor		£40/£50
1960	1,112	Westminster Abbey		£40/£50
1961	1,118	Rochester Cathedral		£40/£50
1962	1,125	Westminster Abbey		£40/£50
1963	1,131	Chelmsford		£40/£50
1964	1,137	Westminster		£40/£50
1965	1,143	Canterbury		£40/£50
1966	1,206	Westminster		£40/£50
1967	986	Durham		£40/£50
1968	964	Westminster		£40/£50
1969	1,002	Selby		£40/£50
1970	980	Westminster		£40/£50
1971	1,018	Tewkesbury Abbey		£40/£50
1972	1,026	York Minster		£45/£55
1973	1,004	Westminster		£45/£55
1974	1,042	Salisbury		£45/£55
1975	1,050	Peterborough		£45/£55
1976	1,158	Hereford		£45/£55
1977	1,138	Westminster		£45/£55
1978	1,178	Carlisle		£40/£50
1979	1,189	Winchester		£40/£50
1980	1,198	Worcester		£40/£50
1981	1,208	Westminster		£40/£50
1982	1,218	St.David's Cathedral		£40/£50
1983	1,218	Exeter Cathedral		£40/£50
1984	1,243	Southwell Minster		£40/£50
1985	1,248	Ripon Cathedral		£40/£50
1986	1,378	Chichester Cathedral		£50/£60
1987	1,390	Ely Cathedral		£50/£60
1988	1,402	Lichfield Cathedral		£50/£60
1989	1,353	Birmingham Cathedral	(63p)	£50/£60
1990	1,523	St. Nicholas Newcastle	(64p)	£50/£60
1991	1,384	Westminster	(65p)	£50/£60
1992		Chester	(66p)	£50/£60
1993		Winchester	(67p)	£75/£85
1994			(68p)	

Averages of Maundy Sets are influenced by V.A.T.
Thus: a set was reported as 'at auction' £65
Investigation showed £65 + Buyer's Premium of
10%, + VAT on the whole - a total of £82.23

Date	Mintage/etc	Fine	V.F.	E.F.	abt Unc/FDC

GEORGE III
Silver - 26 mm until 1816, then 23 mm

Date	Mintage/etc	Fine	V.F.	E.F.	abt Unc/FDC
1763	Northumberland	£100	£250	£350	----
1763	Noted (Seaby 1988)		NEF	£335	----
1764	Pattern (ESC1238)		(Spink 1988)	as struck	£650
1778	A pattern (ESC 1240)		---	£575	----
1786	Proof only	---	---	---	----
1787	No semee of hearts	£2	£10	£20	£30/£40
1787	' ' ' ' no stop overhead		£12	£50	£70/£125
1787	' ' ' ' no stops at date		£12	£55	£75/£150
1787	Hearts in shield	£2	£10	£20	£30/£40
1798	Dorrien & Magens, no stop o/hd (Seaby)		---		£4,000
1816	BULL HEAD 23 mm	£2	£4	£16	£25/£35
1817	23,031,360	£1	£4	£18	£30/£45
1817	GEOE (R over E)	£15	£45	£120	£165/---
1818	1,342,440	£4	£15	£55	£75/£105
1818	Second 8 higher	£6	£28	£100	£160/---
1819	7,595,280	£2	£6.50	£32	£45/---
1819	9 struck over 8	---	£15	£45	£90/---
1819	Noted (Messrs. Weeks 1989 toned gem unc £150)				
1820	7,975,440	£2	£10	£25	£40/£65

GEORGE IV
Laureate Head to 1925; Bare Head from L.o.C.
Rev. SHIELD:

Gnd = Garnished,   Gtd = Gartered.   23mm   L.o.C. = Lion on Crown

Date	Mintage/etc		Fine	V.F.	E.F.	abt Unc/FDC
1820	Pattern	Gnd	(rarity 5)		(1986)	£2,012
1821	2,463,120	Gnd	£3	£12	£40	£60/£100
1821	A proof	Gnd	---	---	---	£400/---
1823	693,000	Gtd	£9	£35	£100	£200/---
1823	A proof	Gtd	---	---	---	£800
1824	4,158,000	Gtd	£3	£12	£35	£55/£75
1825	2,459,160	Gtd	£3	£12	£35	£55/£75
1825	5 struck over 3	Gtd		---	---	----
1825	LION on CROWN rev.		£2	£6	£30	£50/£90
1826	6,351,840	L.o.C.	£2	£6	£25	£40/£65
1826	6 struck over a 2nd 2	L.o.C.		---	---	----
1826	A proof	L.o.C.	(ESC 1258)		---	FDC £200
1827	574,200	L.o.C.	£4	£25	£90	£140/£165
1829	879,120	L.o.C.	£4	£15	£60	£80/£125

Date	Mintage	Fair / Fine	V.F.	E.F.	Unc/abt FDC

WILLIAM IV SILVER 23mm

Date	Mintage	Fair / Fine	V.F.	E.F.	Unc/abt FDC
1831	Proofs, plain edge, from set			£135	£250/£350
1834	3,223,440 grained edge £2.5	£10		£62	£120/£185
1834	A proof with flat topped '3'		(1988)		FDC £600
1835	1,449,360	£3	£12	£65	£125/£190
1836	3,567,960	£3	£10	£50	£70/£120
1837	479,160	£3	£22	£80	£175/- - - -
1837	A proof	- - -	- - -	(1984)	£300

VICTORIA SILVER 23mm

Date	Mintage	Fair / Fine	V.F.	E.F.	Unc/abt FDC
1838	1,956,240	£3	£10	£30	£50/£80
1838	Proofs	- - -	- - -	- - -	£300
1839	5,666,760	£3	£12	£40	£60/£90
1839	Proof (with W.W.) from the sets				£250
1839	No W.W. at neck	£1	£12	£75	£75/£95
1839	Proof (no W.W.) grained edge		- - -		£750
1840	1,639,440	£3 / £6	£25	£100	£125/£200
1841	875,160	£3 / £6	£25	£100	£125/£200
1842	2,094,840	£5	£10	£30	£50/£80
1843	1,465,200	£4	£18	£60	£90/£125
1844	4,466,880	£2	£12	£50	£85/- - -
1845	4,082,760	£2	£14	£35	£50/£95
1846	4,031,280	£2	£14	£35	£50/£95
1848	1,041,480 (*)	£20	£62	£200	£300/- - -
1849	645,480	£2	£12	£50	£95/£150
1850	685,080 but **	£90	£300	£925	£1,500
1850	** 50 over 46	£50	£250	£800	/- - - -
1851	470,071	£15 / £30	£75	£250	£450/- - - -
1852	1,306,574	£2	£12	£50	£75/£95
1853	4,256,188	£2	£12	£50	£75/£95
1853	Proofs from the sets	- - -	- - -		£300/£500

(*) 1848 all 8 struck over 6

Date	Mintage	Fine	V.F.	E.F.	abt Unc/FDC
VICTORIA					
			(continued)		
1854	552,414	£30	£90	£200	£400/ - - -
1855	1,368,499	£2	£12	£40	£70/£85
1856	3,168,000	£2	£12	£40	£70/£85
1857	2,562,120	£2	£12	£40	£70/£85
1857	REG F: Ɔ: (error inverted G)			£165	- - - -
1858	3,108,600	£2	£12	£40	£70/£85
1859	4,561,920	£2	£12	£40	£70/£85
1860	1,671,120	£3	£20	£60	£100/£160
1861	1,382,040	£3	£20	£60	£125/£185
1861	1 over tilted I	(1988 near E.F. £45)			
1862	954,360	£6	£40	£90	£135/£200
1863	859,320	£6	£40	£90	£150/£245
	THE FOLLOWING HAVE A DIE NUMBER (above date)				
1864	4,518,360	£2	£12	£40	£75/£115
1865	5,619,240	£2	£12	£40	£75/£115
	- - - (ESC 1398) Undated pattern Seaby 1988 aFDC £650				
1866	4,989,600	£2	£12	£30	£60/£90
1866	Noted 1993 (Messrs. Weeks) "Gem uncirc."				£85
1866	BBITANNIAR error	- - -	- - -		- - - -
1867	2,166,120	£2	£14	£45	£90/ - - -
1867	Proof without Die No.	- - -	- - -		- - - -
1867	Large head, lower relief	- - -	£200		£275/ - - - -
1868	3,330,360	£2	£12	£40	£90/£125
1869	736,560	£3	£15	£50	£100/£150
1870	1,467,471	£2	£14	£60	£100/£150
1871	4,910,010	£2	£9	£30	£50/£75
1872	8,897,781	£2	£9	£25	£50/£75
1873	6,489,598	£2	£8	£35	£60/£90
1874	5,503,747	£2	£8	£35	£60/£90
1875	4,353,983	£2	£8	£30	£60/£85
1876	1,057,487	£2	£12	£35	£90/£125
1877	2,980,703	£2	£7	£25	£50/£75
1878	3,127,131	£2	£7	£25	£50/£75
1879	3,611,507	£5	£20	£60	£80/£120
1879	6 over 8 (Die 13)		(Numis. Circ.)		May, 1983

Date	Mintage	Fine	V.F.	E.F.	Unc/abt FDC

VICTORIA   DIE NUMBER DISCONTINUED

Date	Mintage	Fine	V.F.	E.F.	Unc/abt FDC
1879	Included page 58	£3	£12	£50	£90/---
1880	4,842,786	£2	£7	£25	£48/£75
1881	5,255,332	£2	£7	£25	£45/£70
1881	Shorter line below SHILLING		£7	£25	£45/£70
1882	1,611,786	£5	£25	£80	£150/---
1883	7,281,450	£2	£6	£15	£40/£55
1884	3,923,993	£2	£7	£15	£30/£45
1885	3,336,527	£2	£7	£18	£35/£50
1886	2,086,819	£1	£5	£14	£35/£50
1887	4,034,133 Young head	£3	£12	£36	£50/£86

Jubilee Head

Date	Mintage	Fine	V.F.	E.F.	Unc/abt FDC
1887	Included above Rev. B	75p	£2	£4	£8/£10
1887	Rev. A	£3	£6	£18	£24/£36
1887	1,084 proofs from the sets	---	---	£50/£75
1888	Last 8 over 7	£3	---	---	---
1888	4,526,856	£1.50	£3	£15	£25/£40
1889	7,039,628 but ★	£10	£45	£200	£365/---
1889	★ Larger head	£2	£3.50	£15	£25/£40
1890	8,794,042	£2	£4	£20	£40/£60
1891	5,665,348	£2	£4	£20	£35/£55
1892	4,591,622	£1	£4	£26	£45/£65

Proofs exist for other dates but are rarely offered.
Messrs. Seaby's "The English Silver Coinage" lists some 40 patterns.

1887 "shuttlecock" varieties : embellishment divides date 18 87
The device points to a rim tooth = Reverse A   Rare
The device points between two teeth = Reverse B   Common

Date	Mintage	Fair/Fine	V.F.	E.F.	abt Unc/FDC

VICTORIA   Old or Widow Head

THREE SHIELDS within GARTER - SILVER - 23mm

Date	Mintage	Fair/Fine	V.F.	E.F.	Unc/FDC
1893	7,039,074	£2	£3	£9	£20/£30
1893	Obv. small letters --		£6	£18	£40/£60
1893	1,312 proofs from the sets				£45/£65
1894	5,953,152	£2	£4	£16	£30/£48
1895	8,880,651	£2	£4	£16	£30/£45
1896	9,264,551	£2	£3	£14	£20/£35
1897	6,270,364	£2	£3	£12	£20/£35
1898	9,768,703	£2	£3	£10	£18/£30
1899	10,965,382	£2	£3	£10	£18/£30
1900	10,937,590	£2	£3	£10	£18/£30
1901	3,426,294	£2	£3	£12	£20/£35

EDWARD VII   Reverse: LION on CROWN - SILVER 23mm

Date	Mintage	Fair/Fine	V.F.	E.F.	Unc/FDC
1902	7,809,481	£1	£2 .	£8	£15/£25
1902	Noted (Messrs Weeks 1989 Toned Gem Unc £23)				
1902	15,123 proofs matt finish			£5	£10/£20
1903	2,061,823	£2	£9	£30	£60/£95
1904	2,040,161	£2	£9	£30	£60/£95
1905	488,390	£18/£25	£75	£250	£500/- --
1906	10,791,025	£1.50	£3	£18	£30/£50
1907	14,083,418	£1.50	£3	£12	£30/£50
1908	3,806,969	£2.50	£9	£40	£60/£95
1909	5,664,982	£2	£5	£40	£60/£100
1910	26,547,236	£1	£3	£10	£20/£30

Date	Mintage	Fine	V.F.	E.F.	Unc/abt FDC

GEORGE V

		SILVER (.925 to 1919 - .500 from 1920)			23mm
1911	20,065,901	- - -	£2	£6	£10/£16
1911	6,007 proofs		- - -	- - -	£28/£35
1912	15,594,009	- - -	£3	£18	£30/£50
1913	9,011,509	£2	£5	£26	£45/£70
1914	23,415,843	- - -	£2	£6	£10/£16
1915	39,279,024	- - -	£2	£4	£9/£14
1916	35,862,015	- - -	£2	£5	£10/£16
1917	22,202,608	- - -	£2	£6	£12/£18
1918	34,915,934	- - -	£2	£6	£10/£16
1919	10,823,824	- - -	£2	£9	£20/£30
		SILVER REDUCED to .500			
1920	22,825,142	- - -	£2	£9	£20/£30
1921	22,648,763	- - -	£3	£15	£25/£40
1922	27,215,738	- - -	£2	£10	£20/£30
1923	14,575,243	- - -	£2	£10	£20/£30
1923	Trial Piece in nickel		- - -	£200	£400

Obv. 1 = above B.M. the neck is hollow.
Obv. 2 = above B.M. the neck is flat.
Rev. A = GEORGĬVS; Rev. B = GEORGĬVS. (see page 65)
1911 Varieties: 1 + A; 1 + B; 2 + A; 2 + B.
1912 Varieties: IMP closely spaced; I M P widely spaced.
1920 Varieties: Obv. 1; Obv. 2.

Date	Mintage	Fine	V.F.	E.F.	abt. Unc/FDC
GEORGE V (continued)			50% SILVER - 50% ALLOY		
1924	Trial in nickel	- - -	- - -	£200	£400
1924	9,250,095	45p	£2.50	£12	£18/£35
1925	A pattern in nickel	- - -	- - -	- - -	
1925	Pattern in lead - obverse has the word MODEL - NVF £175 (1990)				
1925	5,418,764	£1	£5	£20	£36/£62
1926	22,516,453	45p	£2.50	£12	£20/£36
1926	Modified Effigy	- - -	£2.50	£8	£20/£32
1927	9,262,344	- - -	£2.50	£8	£22/£32
1927	NEW DESIGN	- - -	£1.50	£6	£18/£25
1927	15,000 proofs	- - -	- - -	- - -	£18
1928	18,136,778	- - -	65p	£4	£7/£12
1929	19,343,006	- - -	65p	£4	£8/£12
1930	3,137,092	- - -	£3	£12	£24/£36
1931	6,993,926	- - -	75p	£5	£9/£15
1932	12,168,101	- - -	75p	£5	£9/£15
1933	11,511,624	- - -	65p	£4	£6/£10
1934	6,138,463	- - -	£2	£10	£20/£30
1935	9,183,462	- - -	65p	£4	£6/£10
1936	11,910,613	- - -	50p	£3	£5/£9
EDWARD VIII			**(Duke of Windsor)**		
1936 a few Scottish (page 49) no English				- - -	£12,000
GEORGE VI					
			50% SILVER/50% ALLOY until 1947		
1937E	8,359,122	- - -	- - -	£2	£5/£6
1937E	26,402 proofs	-	- - -	- - -	£8
1937S	6,748,875	- - -	- - -	£2	£4/£5
1937S	26,402 proofs	-	- - -	- - -	£8
1938E	4,833,436	- - -	- - -	£4	£14/£18
1938S	4,797,852	- - -	- - -	£4	£12/£16
1939E	11,052,677	- - -	- - -	£1	£4/£6
1939S	10,263,892	- - -	- - -	£1	£4/£6
1940E	11,099,126	- - -	- - -	£1	£4/£6
1940S	9,913,089	- - -	- - -	£1	£4/£6
1941E	11,391,883	- - -	- - -	£1	£4/£6
1941S	8,086,030	- - -	- - -	£2	£5/£7
1942E	17,453,643	- - -	- - -	£1	£3/£4
1942S	13,676,759	- - -	- - -	£1	£3/£4
1943E	11,404,213	- - -	- - -	£1	£3/£4
1943S	9,824,214	- - -	- - -	£1	£3/£4
1944E	11,586,752	- - -	- - -	£1	£3/£4
1944S	10,990,167	- - -	- - -	£1	£3/£4
1945E	15,143,404	- - -	- - -	60p	£2/£3
1945S	15,106,270	- - -	- - -	60p	£2/£3
1946E	18,663,797 see note page 63	- - -	- - -	50p	£2/£3
1946E	Pattern, proof, or trial in cupro-nickel			- - -	- - - -
1946S	16,381,501	- - -	- - -	50p	£2/£3
1947E	12,120,611	- - -	- - -	75p	£3/£4
1947S	12,282,223	- - -	- - -	£1	£4/£6
1948E	45,576,923	- - -	- - -	50p	£2/£4
1948S	45,351,937	- - -	- - -	50p	£2/£4

See note regarding bullion on page 65

Date	Mintage		Fine	V.F.	E.F.	Unc. from/to

GEORGE VI (continued)

Date	Mintage		Fine	V.F.	E.F.	Unc. from/to
1949E	19,328,405		- - -	- - -	£1	£3/£5
1949S	21,243,074		- - -	- - -	£2	£4/£5
1950E	19,243,872		- - -	- - -	£1.50	£4/£5
1950E	17,513	proofs	- - -	- - -	- - -	£6/£7
1950S	14,299,601		- - -	- - -	£1.60	£5/£6
1950S	17,513	proofs	- - -	- - -	- - -	£6/£7
1951E	9,956,930		- - -	- - -	£1	£3/£5
1951E	20,000	proofs	- - -	- - -	- - -	£6/£7
1951S	10,961,174		- - -	- - -	£1	£5/£6
1951S	20,000	proofs	- - -	- - -	- - -	£6/£7
1952E	1 known outside Royal Collection - - -					- - - -

Suffix E = English; and S = Scottish. In 1937 these coins were struck with English, and Scottish, symbols and were circulated, generally, throughout the United Kingdom. The practice continued until 1966; and for 1970.

> Some Heraldic terms:
> RAMPANT - such as lion rampant, page 64, 2nd from left,
> STATANT GUARDANT - the left-hand coin in each row below.
> PASSANT GUARDANT - the three leopards, page 64 at left.
> SEJANT GUARDANT - sitting, facing: right-hand coin each row below.

Passant guardant is sometimes described as couchant (lying down), but the raised paw indicates otherwise. The three leopards are still referred to as such on old coinage, but on modern strikings are likely to be referred to as three lions.

1946E	Reverse A ˙IND	Reverse B ˙˙IND	(see page 65)

Date	Mintage		Fine	V.F.	E.F.	Unc. from/to

ELIZABETH II

CUPRO-NICKEL 23mm

Date	Mintage		Fine	V.F.	E.F.	Unc. from/to
1953E	41,942,894		- - -	- - -	30p	50p/£1
1953E	40,000	proofs	- - -	- - -	FDC	£3/£4
1953S	20,663,528		- - -	- - -	30p	60p/£1
1953S	40,000	proofs	- - -	- - -	FDC	£3/£4
1954E	30,262,032	BRITT. OMN discontinued			45p	£1/£2
1954S	26,771,735		- - -	- - -	36p	£1/£2
1955E	45,259,908		- - -	- - -	36p	£1/£2
1955S	27,950,906		- - -	- - -	36p	£2/£3
1956E	44,907,008		- - -	- - -	£1	£5/£6
1956S	42,853,637		- - -	- - -	£1	£5/£6
1957E	42,774,217		- - -	- - -	25p	£1/£3
1957S	17,959,988		- - -	- - -	£3	£10/£15
1958E	14,392,305		- - -	- - -	£3	£10/£15
1958S	40,822,557		- - -	- - -	25p	50p/£1
1959E	19,442,778		- - -	- - -	25p	50p/£1
1959S	1,012,988		15p	50p	£2	£10/£15
1960E	27,027,914		- - -	- - -	25p	£1/£2
1960S	14,376,932		- - -	- - -	25p	£1/£2
1961E	39,816,907		- - -	- - -	15p	£1/£2
1961S	2,762,558		- - -	10p	75p	£3/£6
1961S	A proof		offered in 1984		- - -	£200
1962E	36,704,379		- - -	- - -		50p/£1
1962S	18,967,310		- - -	- - -		50p/£1
1963E	44,714,000		- - -	- - -		50p/£1
1963S	32,300,000		- - -	- - -		15p/30p
1964E	8,590,900		- - -	- - -		30p/50p
1964S	5,239,100		- - -	- - -		50p/75p
1965E	9,216,000		- - -	- - -		30p/75p
1965S	2,774,000		- - -	- - -		50p/£1
1966E	15,005,000	includes 3,000 minted in 1967				25p/45p
1966S	15,607,000	includes 3,000 minted in 1967				25p/45p
1968	Decimal equivalent FIVE NEW PENCE introduced					
1970E	750,476	proofs for LAST STERLING set				75p/£1
1970S	750,476	proofs for LAST STERLING set				75p/£1

"Pointings" see page 65 · 1953E and 1953S
Obv. 1 = GRATIA · Obv. 2 = GRATIA

1955S   Rev. A = SHILLING

Rev. B = SHILLING

Date	Mintage	Fine	V.F.	E.F.	Unc/abt FDC
GEORGE III	**Bank Token**				Silver 26 mm
1811	Armoured Bust	£3	£9	£25	£35/£60
1811	Proof	--	--	£180	£250
1812	Armoured Bust	£3	£10	£26	£40/£65
1812	Laureate Head	£2	£9	£25	£40/£65
1812	Proof	---	---	£180	£250
1812	Proof with small lettering reverse	---	---	---	£400
1812	Proof in platinum	--	---	---	£500
1813	Laureate Head	£2	£9	£25	£40/£65
1813	Proof in platinum	--	---	---	£500
1814	Laureate Head	£2	£9	£25	£40/£65
1815	Laureate Head	£2	£9	£25	£40/£65
1816	Laureate Head	£2	£9	£25	£40/£65

'Pointings' are very much the key to some varieties. A principal feature such as a letter or ornament is selected and its 'attitude' is used to indicate the use of a different die-punch. Thus HALFPENNY (L̇) indicates that the upright of the 'L' is aimed at a rim bead. HALFPENNY (L̤) that 'L' points between two beads. Many dies are used to complete a full year's striking. New dies are usually identical being from the same, original, punch. Differences are, therefore, interesting numismatically and unequal strikings must, eventually, show up in valuations.

NOTE ON BULLION VALUE: although the collector's value of a worn coin is listed as face-value-only (---), a silver one may have a higher, bullion, value because of the amount of precious metal in it. At one time pre 1947 silver coins were worth 3½ to 4 times face-value and pre 1920 ones up to 7 or 8 times (a worn half-crown might be worth £1). Buyers no longer publish the rate offered: quotations being made on a day-to-day basis. A large enough quantity to sell is necessary to offset the cost of mailing and handling. Check rates on Teletext. Contact the dealer before sending.

		Fine	V.F.	E.F.	abt Unc/FDC
VICTORIA Silver 27 mm					
1848	'GODLESS' (having no DEI GRATIA) patterns £300				£700
1848	As above but with grained (milled) edge		- - -		£2350
1849	413,830 'Godless'	£5	£18	£40	£65/£125
	GOTHIC - date appears in Roman - third column - 30mm.				
1851	1,540 mdcccli	- - - -	- - - -		£2000
1852	1,014,552 mdccclii	£4	£16	£60	£120/£200
1852	ii struck over i (Messrs. Weeks 1993) abtEF £95				- - - -
1853 ★	3,919,950 mdcccliii	£4	£24	£80	£135
1853	Proof	- - - -	- - - -	- - - -	£800
1854	550,413 mdcccliv	£200	£450	£1300	- - - -
1855	831,017 mdccclv	£5	£25	£82	£145/ - - - -
1856 ★	2,201,760 mdccclvi	£5	£26	£95	£160/ - - - -
1857	1,671,120 mdccclvii	£5	£25	£82	£140/£250
1857	Proof (ESC815)	- - - -	- - - -	- - - -	£875
1858 +	2,239,380 mdccclviii	£4	£18	£70	£120/£175
1858	Noted (no stop after date Seaby 1989 EF/GEF £110)				
1859 +	2,568,060 mdccclvix	£4	£24	£80	£135/ - - - -
1860	1,475,100 mdccclx	£5	£30	£110	£180/ - - - -
1862	594,000 mdccclxii	£20	£80	£275	£400/ - - - -
1863	938,520 mdccclxiii	£30	£125	£450	£900/ - - - -
1864	1,861,200 mdccclxiv	£5	£25	£85	£145/ - - - -
1865 !	1,580,044 mdccclxv	£6	£30	£105	£175/ - - - -
1866 !	914,760 mdccclxvi	£6	£30	£105	£180/ - - - -
1867	423,720 mdccclxvii	£15	£60	£200	£340/ - - - -
1868	896,940 mdccclxviii	£5	£25	£82	£145/ - - - -
1869	297,000 mdccclxix	£4	£24	£80	£140/ - - - -
1870	1,080,648 mdccclxx	£4	£24	£80	£140/ - - - -
1871	3,425,605 mdccclxxi	£4	£24	£80	£140/ - - - -
1872	7,199,690 mdccclxxii	£4	£22	£70	£120/ - - - -
1873	5,921,839 mdccclxxiii	£4	£22	£70	£120/£190
1874	1,642,630 mdccclxxiv	£4	£24	£80	£140/ - - - -
1875	1,117,030 mdccclxxv	£4	£24	£80	£140/ - - - -
1876	580,034 mdccclxxvi	£5	£26	£100	£165/ - - - -
1877	682,292 mdccclxxvii	£5	£26	£100	£165/ - - - -
1877	No WW (48 arcs)	£15	£60	£200	- - - - / - - - -
1877	No WW (42 arcs)	£12	£50	£120	£190/ - - - -
1878	1,786,680 mdccclxxviii	£4	£24	£80	£140/ - - - -
1879	1,512,247 mdccclxxix				
Die No.	48 arcs WW (ESC849B)	£30	£80	- - - -	
No Die No.	42 arcs (ESC 850)	£20	£70	(no WW)	- - - -
No Die No.	48 arcs WW (ESC 851)	£7	£25	£75	£165/ - - - -
No WW	38 arcs (ESC 852)	£6	£20	£65	£150/ - - - -
1880	2,167,170 mdccclxxx	£4	£24	£80	£140/ - - - -
1881	2,570,337 mdccclxxxi	£4	£22	£75	£125/ - - - -
1881	Broken die mdccclxxri	£4	£22	£75	£135/ - - - -
1883	3,555,667 mdccclxxxiii	£4	£22	£70	£115/ - - - -
1884	1,447,379 mdccclxxxiv	£4	£22	£70	£115/ - - - -
1885	1,758,210 mdccclxxxv	£4	£22	£75	£120/ - - - -
1886	591,773 mdccclxxxvi	£4	£22	£80	£135/ - - - -
1887	1,776,903 mdccclxxxvii	£7	£30	£130	£225/ - - - -

Those above are inscribed: **one tenth of a pound**
1887 See also 'Jubilee Head' on next page
Proofs exist for many dates; they are rare and rarely offered

Some page 66 varieties - - - - - - - - - - - - - - - - - - - >

Date	Mintage		Fine	V.F.	E.F.	Unc/ abt. FDC.
VICTORIA		**Jubilee Head**				28 mm
1887	Incl page 66		£2	£4	£8	£12/£20
1887	1,084	Jubilee Head proofs			£45	£65/£80
1888	1,541,540		£2	£4	£15	£30/£50
1889	2,973,561		£2	£5	£18	£35/£60
1890	1,684,737		£4	£15	£60	£85/£150
1891	836,438		£6	£25	£75	£115/£185
1892	283,401		£10	£40	£85	£140/£200
		Old, Veiled or Widow Head				
1893	1,666,103		£1.50	£6	£25	£45/£70
1893	1,312	proofs	- - -	- - -	- - -	- -/£125
1894	1,952,842		£2	£8	£30	£45/£75
1895	2,182,968		£2	£7	£28	£40/£65
1896	2,944,416		£2	£7	£28	£40/£65
1897	1,699,921		£2	£4	£25	£40/£60
1898	3,061,343		£2	£4	£25	£40/£60
1899	3,966,953		£2	£4	£25	£40/£55
1900	5,528,630		£2	£4	£25	£40/£55
1901	2,648,870		£2	£4	£24	£40/£55

★ Have varieties with no stop after date. Rarity R2
+ Have varieties with no stop after date. Rarity R
I With colon after date: 1865 R3; 1866 R2
1867 brit: is normal; proofs/patterns have britt:
1874 has variety 'iv struck over iii'. Rarity R2
1887 normal has 33 arcs; variety 46 arcs. Rarity R
R = rare; R2 = very rare; Seaby/Rayner scale.

Date	Mintage	Fine	V.F.	E.F.	abt. Unc/FDC.
EDWARD VII		Britannia standing			Silver 28 mm
1902	2,189,575	£2	£6	£25	£40/£65
1902	15,123	matt finished proofs		---	£20/£45
1903	1,995,298	£3	£12	£35	£55/£90
1904	2,769,932	£5	£15	£50	£100/£150
1905	1,187,596	£14	£45	£160	£300/£460
1906	6,910,128	£2	£10	£40	£80/£120
1907	5,947,895	£2	£10	£40	£90/£140
1908	3,280,010	£4	£14	£70	£140/£200
1909	3,482,289	£4	£14	£70	£140/£200
1910	5,650,713	£2	£8	£40	£80/£120
GEORGE V		From 1920 silver reduced to 50% Shields/Sceptres in Quarters			
1911	5,951,284	---	£4	£20	£35/£55
1911	6,007	proofs ---	---	---	£40/£60
1912	8,571,731	---	£5	£28	£45/£75
1913	4,545,278	---	£5	£30	£45/£75
1914	21,252,701	---	£2	£9	£16/£28
1915	12,367,939	---	£2	£10	£15/£25
1916	21,064,337	---	£2	£9	£15/£25
1917	11,181,617	---	£3	£12	£20/£30
1918	29,211,792	---	£2	£7	£15/£25
1919	9,469,292	---	£3	£11	£20/£32
1920	15,387,833	(.500 silver)	£3	£15	£30/£45
1921	34,863,895	£2	£3	£6	£18/£25
1922	23,861,044	£2	£5	£9	£20/£30
1923	21,546,533	£2	£6	£12	£25/£38
1924	4,582,372	£2	£5	£20	£40/£60
1925	1,404,136	£5	£12	£70	£135/£210
1925	Uniface pattern in lead (Seaby 1990) VF+ £225				

1911
Two obverses
see page 18

1914
Large rim teeth
and small teeth

1920
BRITT and BRITT

| | | | | | Unc/abt. |
| Date | Mintage | Fine | V.F. | E.F. | FDC. |

GEORGE V   (continued)

Date	Mintage	Fine	V.F.	E.F.	Unc/abt. FDC.
1926	5,125,410	£2	£6	£25	£40/£65
1927	15,000 proofs of new design			- - -	£35/£50
1928	11,087,186	£2	£3	£6	£10/£15
1929	16,397,279	£2	£4	£7	£10/£15
1930	5,753,568	£2	£4	£6	£12/£18
1931	6,556,331	£2	£4	£6	£10/£18
1932	717,041	£3	£15	£60	£120/£180
1933	8,685,303	£2	£3	£6	£10/£18
1934	none	- - -	- - -	- - -	- - -/- - -
1935	7,540,546	£2	£3	£7	£10/£18
1936	9,897,448	£2	£4	£8	£12/£20

EDWARD VIII as GEORGE VI but monogram ER (page 49)

GEORGE VI   50/50 silver/alloy until 1947 - 28 mm

Date	Mintage	Fine	V.F.	E.F.	Unc/abt. FDC.
1937	13,006,781	- - -	- - -	£2	£3/£5
1937	26,402 proofs	- - -	- - -	- - -	£8/£10
1938	7,909,388	- - -	- - -	£5	£12/£16
1939	20,850,607	- - -	- - -	£3	£4/£5
1939	Proof	- - -	(Spinks 1986)		/£165
1940	18,700,338	- - -	- - -	£2	£3/£5
1941	24,451,079	- - -	- - -	£2	£3/£4
1942	39,895,243	- - -	- - -	£2	£3/£4
1943	26,711,987	- - -	- - -	£2	£3/£4
1944	27,560,005	- - -	- - -	£2	£3/£4
1945	25,858,049	- - -	- - -	£2	£3/£4
1946	22,910,085	- - -	- - -	£2	£3/£4

CUPRO-NICKEL

Date	Mintage	Fine	V.F.	E.F.	Unc/abt. FDC.
1946	Trial Piece in cupro-nickel, for new coinage				- - - -
1947	22,910,085	- - -	- - -	80p	£2/£3
1948	67,553,636	- - -	- - -	70p	£2/£3
1949	28,614,939	- - -	- - -	£1.50	£4/£6
1949	Proof	- - -	- - -	- - -	£160/- - -
1950	24,357,490	- - -	- - -	£1.60	£4/£6
1950	17,513 proofs	- - -		- - -	£8/- -
1951	27,411,747	- - -	- - -	£1.65	£5/£8
1951	20,000 proofs	- - -	- - -	- - -	£8/- -

Date	Mintage		Fine	V.F.	E.F.	abt. Unc/FDC
ELIZABETH II					Cupro-nickel	28 mm
1953	11,958,710		- - -	- - -	65p	£2/£4
1953	40,000	proofs	- - -	- - -	- - -	£4/£6
1954	13,085,422		- - -	- - -	£5	£20/£40
1955	25,887,253		- - -	- - -	60p	£1/£3
1956	47,824,500		- - -	- - -	60p	£2/£3
1957	33,071,282		- - -	- - -	£2	£12/£25
1958	9,564,580		- - -	- - -	£1	£6/£12
1958	Proof		(1993)	V.I.P. proof		FDC £250
1959	14,080,319		- - -	- - -	£2	£12/£30
1960	13,831,782		- - -	- - -	50p	£1/£3
1961	37,735,315		- - -	- - -	50p	£1/£3
1962	35,147,903		- - -	- - -	30p	£1/£3
1963	25,562,000		- - -	- - -	20p	£1/£3
1964	16,539,000		- - -	- - -	20p	£1/£3
1965	48,163,000		- - -	- - -	20p	50p/£2
1966	84,041,000		- - -	- - -	20p	50p/£2
1967	22,152,000		- - -	- - -	20p	50p/£2
1968	17,566,000	dated 1967.		Decimals Introduced.		
1970	750,476	proofs for Last Sterling set				£2

Continued on page 90 under DECIMAL COINAGE

HALF DOLLARS

Date	Details	Fine	V.F.	E.F.
Half Dollars are Countermarked 4 reales				33 mm
Oval countermarks of George III		£60	£150	£300

PIECES OF FOUR, which is what these are, doesn't have the same 'ring' as PIECES OF EIGHT. Half Dollars are virtually identical to the coin shown on page 78 except 8R is replaced by 4R (or 4 to right of shield in some types) and, of course, the small difference in diameter. Apart from Reales, other large silver coins were used after being countermarked.

Date	Mintage		Fine	V.F.	E.F.	abt Unc/FDC

GEORGE III
Silver 32 mm

Date	Mintage		Fine	V.F.	E.F.	abt Unc/FDC
1816	Bull Head		£4	£16	£64	£80/£144
1816	Proof		---	---	---	£1,000
1817	8,092,656		£4	£16	£64	£80/£144
1817	Smaller head		£5	£20	£70	£95/£160
1817	D of DEI over T	---	(at auction 1987)			£325/----
1818	2,905,056		£6	£20	£70	£160/£200
1819	4,790,016		£6	£20	£70	£160/£200
1820	2,396,592		£8	£24	£90	£180/£250

(inc 1820 George IV) Proofs exist for each date

GEORGE IV
Silver 32 mm

Date	Mintage		Fine	V.F.	E.F.	abt Unc/FDC
1820	Garnished Shield		£4	£25	£85	£175/----
1821	1,435,104		£5	£26	£90	£175/£290
1821	Proof		---	---	£300	£525/£700
1822	Proof (only 2 known)			1993	FDC	£3,650
1823	2,003,760		£150	£500	£1800	£3,000
1823	Shield in Garter		£6	£25	£115	£130/£275
1823	Pattern	(ESC 652)		1991	FDC	£4,800
1824	465,696 ?		£8	£35	£140	£225/£350
1824	Bare Head		£200	£750	£2650	----/----
1825	2,258,784		£7	£28	£80	£160/£200
1825	Proofs	(ESC 643; and 644)				/£850
1825	Proof (ESC 645) in Barton's Metal : a sandwich of copper and two skins of gold.				(1984)	£1,500
1826	2,189,088		£6	£24	£96	£120/£216
1826	Proofs from the sets			---	£150	£250/£400
1828	49,890 ?		£10	£40	£175	£300/----
1829	508,464		£9	£36	£150	£265/£350

Proofs except 1828 and 1829; patterns 1820/22/23/24

Pattern "Binfield" (ESC 655) 1991 abt.Unc. £395/----

WILLIAM IV
Silver 32 mm

Date	Mintage		Fine	V.F.	E.F.	abt Unc/FDC
1831	Proofs from the sets (noted 1989 GEF £275)					----/----
1834 ★	993,168 WW		£10	£40	£150	£275/£400
1834 ★	WW in script		£4	£24	£90	£200/£290
1835	281,952		£9	£40	£125	£200/£350
1836	1,588,752		£6	£24	£96	£120/£200
1836	6 struck over 5		£9	£45	£100	£150/£250
1837	150,526		£10	£40	£160	£200/£360

1834 ★ proofs for both types of signature

abt.

Date	Mintage	Fine	V.F.	E.F.	Unc/FDC.
VICTORIA	*Young Head*				Silver 32 mm
1839	Raised WW (at neck)		£600	£2250	ornamental fillets
1839	Incuse (struck In) WW		£550	£2000	plain fillets
1839	Proofs from the sets	---		£150	£300/£450
1840	386,496	£12	£50	£125	£200/£300
1841	42,768	£20	£85	£300	£600/----
1842	486,288	£7	£35	£100	£175/£275
1843	454,608	£16	£60	£200	£300/£450
1844	1,999,008	£6	£25	£90	£150/£240
1845	2,231,856	£6	£25	£90	£150/£240
1846	1,539,668	£6	£25	£90	£150/£240
1848	367,488 8/6	£30	£120	£360	£475/£650
1849	261,360 large date	£10	£50	£175	£250/£360
1849	Smaller date	£12	£55	£200	£275/£375
1850	484,613	£8	£42	£175	£350/----
1853	Proofs from the sets (ESC 687)			---	£1,500
1862	Proofs (ESC 688) and (ESC 689)			---	£2,500
1864	Proof only, for the Albert Memorial			---	£3,000
1874	2,188,599	£4	£20	£70	£130/----
1875	1,113,483	£4	£22	£75	£145/----
1876	633,221	£4	£24	£80	£150/----
1876	6 struck over 5	---	---	---	----
1877	447,059	£4	£16	£60	£90/£140
1878	1,466,232	£4	£16	£60	£90/£140
1879	901,356	£5	£20	£80	£140/£220
1879	Proof (ESC704)		(Seaby	1990	abtFDC) £1100
1880	1,346,350	£4	£20	£60	£90/£140
1881	2,301,495	£4	£14	£50	£90/£140
1882	808,227	£4	£25	£75	£125/£200
1883	2,982,779	£4	£16	£60	£120/----
1884	1,569,175	£4	£20	£65	£120/----
1885	1,628,438	£4	£20	£65	£120/----
1886	891,767	£4	£20	£75	£120/£200
1887	1,438,046 Yng.Head	£4	£22	£75	£120/£200
1887	JUBILEE HEAD	£2	£5	£9	£15/£25
1887	1,084 proofs	--	---	---	£125/£145

Date	Mintage	Fine	V.F.	E.F.	Unc/abt. FDC.

VICTORIA — Jubilee Head (continued)

Date	Mintage	Fine	V.F.	E.F.	Unc/abt. FDC.
1888	1,428,787	£3	£6	£25	£40/£65
1889	4,811,954	£3	£5	£20	£30/£50
1890	3,228,111	£3	£10	£35	£50/£75
1891	2,284,632	£3	£10	£30	£55/£80
1892	1,710,946	£3	£10	£30	£50/£75

Old or Widow Head

1893	1,792,600	£2	£7	£20	£30/£50
1893	1,312 proofs		- - -	- - -	£110
1894	1,524,960	£3	£9	£40	£50/£70
1895	1,772,662	£3	£7	£30	£40/£60
1896	2,148,505	£3	£7	£30	£40/£60
1897	1,678,643	£3	£7	£25	£35/£55
1898	1,870,055	£3	£7	£30	£40/£60
1899	2,863,872	£3	£7	£30	£40/£60
1900	4,479,128	£3	£7	£20	£30/£50
1901	1,516,570	£3	£7	£20	£30/£50

Several patterns, proofs and varieties occur.

EDWARD VII — SILVER 32mm

1902	1,316,008	£2	£6	£20	£30/£50
1902	15,123 matt surfaced proofs			- - -	£45/£65
1903	274,840	£20	£75	£225	£450/£625
1904	709,652	£9	£45	£200	£300/£400
1905	166,008	£65	£200	£700	£900/- - -
1906	2,886,206	£3	£8	£40	£75/£120
1907	3,693,930	£3	£9	£40	£75/£120
1908	1,758,889	£4	£15	£60	£95/£165
1909	3,051,592	£3	£12	£50	£80/£130
1910	2,557,685	£3	£9	£40	£70/£100

Proofs noted: 1890 £350; 1864 £825; 1876 £1,250.

Date	Mintage	Fine	V.F.	E.F.	Unc/FDC
GEORGE V	SILVER to 1920; then 50/50 SILVER/ALLOY				
1911	2,914,573	---	£5	£20	£40/£60
1911	6,007 proofs	---	---		£60/£70
1912	4,700,789	---	£5	£25	£50/£75
1913	4,090,160	---	£7	£30	£60/£90
1914	18,333,003	---	---	£10	£20/£30
1915	32,433,066	---	---	£10	£20/£30
1916	29,530,020	---	---	£10	£15/£25
1917	11,172,052	---	£2	£12	£25/£35
1918	29,079,592	---	---	£7	£14/£22
1919	10,266,737	---	---	£15	£25/£36
NOW REDUCED TO .500 SILVER					
1920	17,983,077			£15	£30/£45
1921★	23,677,889	---	---	£15	£25/£40
1922★★	16,396,774	---	---	£15	£30/£45
1923	26,308,526	---	---	£10	£16/£25
1924	5,866,294	---	---	£15	£30/£50
1925	1,413,461	£3	£15	£100	£150/£250
1926	4,473,516	---	---	£30	£45/£75
1926	No colon after OMN	£5	£25	£165	£260/----
1926	Modified Effigy (see page 45)	£4	£30	£50/£75
1927	6,852,872	---	---	£10	£20/£35
1927	15,000 proofs, new design	---	--	£20/£30
1928	18,762,727	---	---	£6	£10/£16
1929	17,632,636	---	---	£6	£10/£16
1930	809,501	£3	£10	£60	£120/£180
1931	11,264,468	---	---	£6	£10/£16
1932	4,793,643	---	---	£15	£25/£40
1933	10,311,494	---	---	£7	£14/£21
1934	2,422,399	---	---	£20	£30/£65
1935	7,022,216	---	---	£6	£10/£16
1935	A proof changed hands in 1975 for			£160/----
1936	7,039,423	---	---	£5	£8/£14

1921★   Varieties DEI and DEÏ (see pointings page 65)
1922★★   Crown rests on shield (thin groove) = Rev. A
              Wide groove twixt crown and shield = Rev. B

       1928   Rosette: ★ = Rev. A;   ★ = Rev. B
       1929   Varieties as for 1928

Date	Mintage		Fine	V.F.	E.F.	Unc/abt FDC

EDWARD VIII *(Duke of Windsor)* ·500 SILVER
1937 Standard bearing Royal Arms (page 49) £16,000

GEORGE VI .500 SILVER until 1947 - 32mm

Date	Mintage		Fine	V.F.	E.F.	Unc/abt FDC
1937	9,106,440		--	--	£2	£5/£7
1937	26,402	proofs	--	--	--	---/£10
1938	6,426,478		--	£1	£3	£12/£17
1939	15,478,635		--	--	£2	£5/£8
1940	17,948,439		--	--	£3	£6/£9
1941	15,773,984		--	--	£2	£5/£7
1942	31,220,090		--	--	£2	£4/£6
1943	15,462,875		--	--	£2	£5/£7
1944	15,255,165		--	--	£2	£3/£5
1945	19,849,242		--	--	£1	£3/£5
1946	22,724,873		--	--	£1	£3/£5
			NOW CUPRO-NICKEL (no silver)			
1947	21,911,484		--	--	£1	£2/£4
1948	71,164,703		--	--	£1	£2/£4
1949 ★	28,272,512		--	--	£1	£5/£8
1950	28,335,500		--	--	£1	£5/£7
1950	17,513	proofs	--	--	--	£8/£10
1951	9,003,520		--	--	£1.50	£4/£6
1951	20,000	proofs	--	--	--	£6/£9
1952	1	Sold by "Private Treaty" in 1991				£28,500

★ IND: IMP (Emperor of India)
discontinued from 1949

Q.E.II values
on page 76

Date	Mintage	Fine	V.F.	E.F.	Unc/FDC.

ELIZABETH II   pictures page 75   CUPRO-NICKEL 32mm

Date	Mintage		Fine	V.F.	E.F.	Unc/FDC.
1953	4,333,214		--	--	75p	£1.5/£2.5
1953	40,000	proofs	--	--	--	£5/£7
1954	11,614,953		--	--	£4	£15/£25
1954	Proof		--	--	(1985)	/£225
1955	23,628,726		--	--	80p	£3/£4
1956	33,934,909		--	--	80p	£3/£4
1957	34,200,563		--	--	50p	£2/£3
1958	15,745,668		--	--	£3	£12/£20
1959	9,028,844		--	--	£4	£25/£30
1960	19,929,191		--	--	75p	£3/£4
1961	25,887,897		--	--	--	£1
1962	24,013,312		--	--	--	£1
1963	17,557,600		--	--	--	£1
1964	5,973,600		--	--	45p	£2
1965	9,878,400		--	--	--	£1
1966	13,384,000		--	--	--	70p
1967	18,895,200		--	--	--	45p
1968	14,163,200	but dated 1967	--	--		
1969	Halfcrowns were demonetized		31st December.			
1970	Proofs from the 8-coin set		--	--		£2.00

THREE SHILLINGS

GEORGE III   BANK OF ENGLAND TOKENS   SILVER 34/35mm

VALUE and DATE enclosed by OAKWREATH: varying acorn count

Date	Description	Fine	V.F.	E.F.	Unc/FDC.
1811	Acorns number 26	£5	£15	£40	£55/£95
1811	Acorns numbering 24, 25, or 27; also proofs				- - - -
1811	(ESC 410) obverse A2 + reverse with 26 acorns				/£500
1812	Armoured bust (ESC 415)	£5	£15	£45	£65/£110
1812	Laureate head (ESC 416)	£4	£12	£36	£55/£90
1812	Obverse B1 (ESC 417) oak/olive wreath, proof				£475
1813	Similar to illustration	£4	£12	£36	£55/£90
1814	Similar to illustration	£4	£12	£35	£55/£90
1815	Similar to illustration	£4	£12	£35	£55/£90
1816	Similar to illustration	£80	£165	£300	£400/£600

Date	Mintage		Fine	V.F.	E.F.	abt. Unc/FDC
VICTORIA		**Jubilee Head**				SILVER 36mm
1887	483,347 Roman I		£4	£8	£16	£22/£45
1887	Roman I proof		- -	- -	- - -	£150/£200
1887	Arabic 1 in date		£4	£8	£16	£22/£45
1887	Arabic 1 proof		- -	- -	- - -	£150/£200
1888	243,340		£5	£10	£25	£50/£85
1888 ★	Inverted 1 for second I	£6	£20	£55	£125/£180
1889	1,185,111		£4	£8	£16	£32/£50
1889 ★	Inverted 1 for second I	£7	£22	£65	£130/£195
1890	782,146		£5	£12	£25	£50/£75
1890	Pattern with reverse worded	DOUBLE FLORIN				- - -

★ 2nd I of VICTORIA   J.E.B. at truncation = Designer/Engraver Joseph Boehm

GEORGE V
SILVER 36mm
1910	Double Florin in gold	- - -	(1986)	£5,700
1911	Rare Plain and grained edge patterns (sundry metals)
1911	As picture but DOUBLE FLORIN (1989 abtFDC £450)
1914	With the words TWELVE GROATS and in various metals

GEORGE VI   SILVER 36mm
| 1950 | Patterns, grained edge,   George and Dragon   ext. rare |
| 1950 | Similar to previous coin but FOUR SHILLINGS on edge |

78   SILVER DOLLARS   (4/9d; 5/-; or 5/6d !)

(Face Value 4/9d: thus "Two King's Heads not worth a Crown")

Date	Fine	V.F.	E.F.	Unc.

GEORGE III

COUNTERMARKED SPANISH 8 REALES   39/40mm

Oval mark from hallmark punch	£50	£100	£225	(ESC129)
Noted (Coin V.F. Cmk E.F. Spink 1988)		£150	- - - -	(ESC129)
Noted (Coin nV.F. Cmk GVF Seaby 1990)		£120	- - - -	(ESC129)
Octagonal mark from Maundy punch	£90	£175	£600	- - - -
Oval mark on Louis XVI half-ECU		(1976)	£700	- - - -
1798 octagonal c/mk Fine	£190		(Grantham Coins 1993)	

A 'PIECE OF EIGHT' showing oval countermark

BANK OF ENGLAND DOLLARS   Unc/FDC

1804	FIVE SHILLINGS	(ESC 144)	£20	£80 £150	£200/£300
1804		(ESC 149)		GVF £95	- - - -
1804	Thick flan (similar ESC 165)		(1980)		£3000

PATTERNS:

1804	Garter Dollar	(ESC 182)	(1990)	£750	- - - -
1804	Garter Dollar	(ESC 185)	(1984)	- - - -	£1500
1804	Garter Dollar	(ESC 186)	(1980)	- - - -	£4000
1811	Oakwreath Dollar	(ESC 206 5/6d)	(1983)	£600	- - - -

Date	Mintage		Fine	V.F.	E.F.	Unc/abt. FDC
GEORGE III		*LAUREATE HEAD*				SILVER 38mm
1818	155,232	LVIII	£8	£25	£100	£175/£250
1818		LIX	£8	£25	£100	£150/£250
1819	683,496	LIX	£8	£25	£100	£150/£250
1819	9 over 8	LIX	£20	£70	£200	£400/£500
1819	No edge stops	LIX	£20	£60	£165	£350/£475
1819		LX	£8	£30	£95	£150/£240
1819	No stop after TUTAMEN	£12	£42	£160		£300/£450
1820	448,272	LX	£8	£30	£120	£200/£275
1820	20 over 19	LX	£15	£60	£130	£300/£450
1820	Undated pattern (ESC221) by Webb & Mills (1991)					£495

Patterns greatly prized. THE THREE GRACES (1980)   £3,500
A set (3) (silver, tin, encapsulated tin) Spinks 1984   £12,500

abt.

Date	Mintage	Fine	V.F.	E.F.	Unc/FDC
GEORGE IV *Laureate Head*					SILVER 38mm
1821	437,976 SECVNDO	£10	£30	£150/£200	£300/£500
1821	SECVNDO proof	---	(1989)	£2250	
1821	Error TERTIO proof	---	---	(1989)	£3300
1822	124,929 SECVNDO	£15	£60	£350	£950/£1300
1822	SECVNDO proof	---	---	(1986)	£2500
1822	TERTIO	£14	£70	£200	£500/£750
1822	TERTIO proof	---	---	(1986)	£2300
1823	Without edge number, proof only (offers to buy £6000)				
1825	(ESC 255) BARE HEAD pattern ---		(1981)		£3800
1826	(ESC 257) SEPTIMO proof from the sets		(1987)		£3000
1828	Pattern in Germanic style		(1983)	£400	-----

Date	Mintage	Fine	V.F.	E.F.	Abt. Unc/FDC

WILLIAM IV

MANTLE design as halfcrown- SILVER 38 mm

Date	Mintage	Fine	V.F.	E.F.	Abt. Unc/FDC
1831	W.W. (ESC 271) (near FDC, minor defects, Seaby £2750)				
1831	W.W. Proof in gold (collected as £5 pieces)				/£7500
1831	W.Wyon (ESC 273)	---	---	£3000	/£4500
1832	Lead Pattern, extreme rarity edge TERTIO		£2000		----
1834	A plain edged proof	---	----		/£6500

VICTORIA   *YOUNG HEAD*   SILVER 38 mm

Date	Mintage	Fine	V.F.	E.F.	Abt. Unc/FDC
1837	Incuse Pattern (see page 83) Auction (1987)				£2600
1837	Pattern, lead, mirror image (Spink 1988)				£650
1839	Proofs from the sets (ESC 279)		£800	£1200/£2000	
1844	94,248 Edge VIII :				
	Star-shaped edge stops £10	£40	£200	£750/£1000	
1844	Proof with star-shaped edge stops	---	----		/£4000
1844	Cinquefoil (five leaves) stops		£50	£400	£1200/£1600
1845	159,192 Edge VIII	£10	£40	£200	£750/£1000
1846	Pattern by W.Wyon (ESC 341)	---	(1980)		/£3000
1847	140,976 Edge XI	£16	£70	£360	£750/£1000
1847	8,000 UNDECIMO proof GOTHIC		£560	£1000/£1500	
1847	"Superb example ..... practically as struck" Glendinings '92				£1705
1847	Noted (2 in gold, Spink-Taisel 1988)	the pair £113,000			
1847	Error edge SEPTIMO proof GOTHIC	----		-----	
1847	Without edge number (ESC 291)		£600	£1200/£1600	
1853	460 D.SEPTIMO from the sets		£2000	£3000/£4000	
1853	"Magnificent Gem FDC" Whiteaves-Scott '93				£4250
1853	Without edge number (ESC 294)		----	£4500/£6000	
1879	Return to Young Head. Offers for this exceed				£15,000

Reverse: ST. GEORGE and THE DRAGON

			Fine	V.F.	E.F.	abt Unc/FDC
Date	Mintage					

VICTORIA Jubilee Head
GOLDEN JUBILEE

Date	Mintage		Fine	V.F.	E.F.	abt Unc/FDC
1887	173,581		£5	£10	£20	£30/£50
1887	1,084	proofs	- -	- - -	£150	£250/£360
1888	131,899	close date	£7	£21	£40	£65/£110
1888		wider date	£8	£25	£60	£125/- - - -
1889	1,807,223		£5	£10	£25	£45/£65
1890	997,862		£7	£18	£40	£65/£95
1891	566,394		£7	£18	£40	£65/£95
1892	451,334		£8	£22	£60	£100/£145

Prices asked often have wide variations, for example:
1887 ABU £24; BU £40; BU Gem £50; FDC £75.

VICTORIA Old, Veiled or Widow Head

Date	Mintage		Fine	V.F.	E.F.	abt Unc/FDC
1893	1,312	LVI proofs from the sets			£150	£275/£375
1893	497,845	LVI	£5	£20	£45	£95/£145
1893		LVII	£10	£25	£75	£165/£250
1894	144,906	LVII	£6	£30	£90	£175/- - - -
1894		LVIII	£6	£20	£80	£160/- - - -
1895	252,862	LVIII	£6	£20	£80	£150/- - - -
1895		LIX	£6	£20	£80	£150/- - - -
1896	317,599	LIX	£8	£25	£125	£250/£375
1896		LX	£6	£20	£60	£80/£150
1897	262,118	LX	£6	£20	£60	£80/£150
1897		LXI	£5	£18	£55	£75/£145
1898	161,450	LXI	£10	£30	£90	£180/£275
1898		LXII	£6	£20	£60	£120/£180
1899	166,300	LXII	£6	£20	£60	£120/£180
1899		LXIII	£6	£20	£60	£120/£180
1900	353,356	LXIII	£5	£18	£45	£90/£130
1900		LXIV	£5	£18	£45	£90/£130

EDWARD VII

Date	Mintage		Fine	V.F.	E.F.	abt Unc/FDC
1902	256,020		£15	£25	£50	£75/£100
1902	15,123	proofs having a matt surface			£65	£85/£110
1902 ★	Pattern	depicting Edward VII, robed, and on horseback				
1902	Pattern	similar to the previous entry, struck in gold				

★ 1902 Style as Charles I "Tower" Crown (Spinks 1985) £2,500

CROWN PATTERNS: there are some
45 varieties, from a modernistic and
incuse young head, to a heavily
ornamented old style (both shown)

CROWNS

Date	Mintage	Fine	V.F.	E.F.	abt. Unc/FDC.
GEORGE V		*debased silver of .500 fineness from 1927*			
1910	Pattern:		flowing interpretation George/Dragon		
1910	Similar but date in exergue reverse (ESC 389)				£3,500
1927	15,030 proofs from the sets	- - -		£60	£90/£100
1928	9,034	£20	£40	£70	£95/£160
1928	Noted (1991)	(J.Welsh Gem BU/FDC)			£150
1929	4,994	£25	£50	£90	£120/£200
1930	4,847	£25	£50	£90	£125/£240
1931	4,056	£30	£60	£120	£165/£290
1932	2,395	£40	£65	£140	£200/£300
1932	4 proofs	One noted	GEF/FDC (1986)		£950
1933	7,132	£30	£50	£90	£125/£225
1934	932	£250	£450	£750	£900/£1500
1934	8 proofs	as far back as 1976			£875
1935	714,769 incuse edge lettering			£5	£9/£14
1935	Superior strikings, in special box	- - -			£20/£30
1935	2,500 silver proofs, raised edge lettering				£200/£280
1935 ★	Some; both incuse and raised, have edge lettering error				
1935 ★★	30 proofs struck in gold		- - -		£7750
1935	A few .925 proofs incuse edge lettering				£1750
1935	A pattern - date in front of horse's head				- - - -
1936	2,473	£40	£70	£140	£200/£250
1936	3 or 4 proofs are thought to exist				- - - -

★ correct order of words: DECUS ET TUTAMEN ANNO REGNI

★★ gold proofs have raised edge lettering

EDWARD VIII   *.500 fine silver*   38 mm

1936	Unofficial patterns	- - -	- - -	FDC	£15
1936	Noted 1993	- - -	- - -	abt FDC	£14.50
1937	designs similar to those of George VI			Pages 49 and 85	

Date	Mintage		Fine	V.F.	E.F.	Abt. Unc/ FDC.

GEORGE VI

.500 fine silver — 38 mm

1937	418,699	Coronation	- - -	£5	£9	£12/ £20
1937	26,402	Proofs from the sets				£25/ £35
1937		Proofs with special frosting (V.I.P.)		- -		/ £800

Cupro - nickel — 38 mm

1951	1,983,540	Festival of Britain Prooflike		£2	£5/ £7
*	*	Available in box of issue, choice of green or purple
1951	★	Patterns (or special proofs) (K.B.Coins 1990) FDC £450
1951		2 proofs on unedged blanks (1987)	£700

★ Not to be confused with 'prooflike' issue

ELIZABETH II

Cupro - nickel — 38 mm

1953	5,962,621	Equestrian	- - -		50p	£2/ £3
1953	40,000	Proofs from sets and Maundy				£10/ £25
1953	★	Noted (Special proofs) (K.B.Coins 1992)			FDC £395
1953	Pattern	All-over frosting, dismal/matt			but very rare
1953	Large date	Large emblems on cross		- -		£265
1960	1,024,038	British Trades Fair	- -	£1		£5/ £7
1960	70,000	Polished die specials		£2/ £4		£7/ £10
1960	★	Noted	V.I.P. Proof (K.B.Coins 1992)			FDC £475
1965	19,640,000	Churchill	- - -	- - -		40p/ 65p
1965	Noted	Satin finish "special" (K.B.Coins 1990) FDC £560

★ Frosted detail, highly polished field,
not to be confused with 'ordinary' or polished die proofs.

Pictures of Elizabeth II CROWNS on page 86

For DECIMAL CROWNS (25p) see page 91

Valuations for these coins, on page 85.

Smith's Private Pattern Decimals

1, 2, 5 and 10 cents	inverted reverse	£900
1, 2, 5 and 10 cents restrikes	upright reverse	£300

VICTORIA

DECIMAL 'FARTHING' of 1854   1/1000 of £1   a MILLE
1854 (Noted 1990 as struck)   MODEL MILLE, GOTHIC HEAD, £125

VICTORIA

DECIMAL PATTERNS of 1857   BRITANNIA Reverse   BRONZE
Legend above Britannia: Legend below Britannia:

A)	ONE CENT	MDCCCLVII		16.5mm
B)	HALF FARTHING	ONE CENTIME		17.0mm
C)	TWO CENTS	MDCCCLVII		22.0mm
D)	ONE FARTHING	TWO CENTIMES		22.0mm
E)	FIVE CENTS	MDCCCLVII		27.0mm
F)	DECIMAL HALFPENNY	5 CENTIMES		27.5mm
G)	DECIMAL HALFPENNY	MDCCCLVII		27.0mm
H)	FIVE FARTHINGS	10 CENTIMES		33.5mm
H)	(Noted 1989 about V.F.)	FIVE FARTHINGS		£125
I)	DECIMAL PENNY	ONE TENTH OF A SHILLING		32.5mm
J)	TEN CENTS	ONE TENTH OF A SHILLING		32.5mm

VICTORIA

DECIMAL PATTERNS of 1859   DATE BELOW HEAD   BRONZE

K)	HALF DECIMAL PENNY	In wreath oak leaves/acorns	27mm
L)	HALF DECIMAL PENNY	ONE TWENTIETH SHILLING	27mm
M)	ONE DECIMAL PENNY	In wreath oak leaves/acorns	32mm
M)	(Noted 1986 E.F.)	Cupro-nickel and tin	£400
N)	ONE TENTH OF DECIMAL PENNY	A SHILLING	32mm
O)	★ DECIMAL PENNY ★	ONE TENTH OF A SHILLING	32mm
O2)	Has larger lettering and date between ornaments		32mm
O2)	(Noted 1986 E.F.)	Nickel-bronze	£250
P)	ONE DECIMAL PENNY	wreath laurel leaves/berries	32mm
Q)	As P) but wreath half palm leaves, half oak leaves		32mm
R)	ONE DECIMAL PENNY	lion, shield, flags, bee-hive	32mm
S)	DECIMAL PENNY	crown, trident, laurel/oak wreath	32mm

See trident of 1961 2 CENTS

VICTORIA

DECIMAL PATTERNS of 1859   SIZE REDUCED   BRONZE

T)	DECIMAL HALF PENNY	laurel wreath with berries
U)	DECIMAL HALF PENNY	half laurel, half oak, crown
V)	DECIMAL HALF PENNY	complete circle of palm leaves
W)	ONE DECIMAL PENNY In exergue	lion and palm tree
X)	DECIMAL 1 PENNY	below large trident with dolphins
Y)	ONE PENNY Una and the Lion DECIMAL in exergue	
Z)	ONE DECIMAL PENNY	wreath alternating oak & laurel
Z2)	ONE DECIMAL PENNY	wreath half oak, half laurel
Z3)	Circle of roses, shamrocks, thistles around ONE DECIMAL PENNY	

First three 19.5 mm;   W) to Z3) 27 mm.
Coins without date, or without denomination, not listed.

VICTORIA   *Silver Patterns 1848 ONE TENTH OF A POUND 27 mm*

1) Trident, wreath of oak leaves, 100 MILLES - ONE DECADE
2) Trident, wreath of oak leaves, 100 MILLES - ONE CENTUM
3) Trident   -   wreath of oak leaves   -   ONE FLORIN
4) Royal cypher VR - emblems intertwined - ONE DECADE
4)   ONE DECADE   (1988 as struck)   £725
5) Royal cypher VR - emblems intertwined - ONE CENTUM
5)   ONE CENTUM   (Spink 1988 GEF)   £695
6) Royal cypher VR - emblems intertwined - ONE FLORIN
7) Cruciform shields - rose at centre, below - ONE DIME
            Each of the seven with three different obverses (!)
8) Cruciform shields - laureate head   -   date below
9) Cruciform shields - plain hair binding   -   date below
10) 1848 Cruciform shields   - crowned bust   -   Godless florin
11) 1851 As 1848 but in Gothic style: the date as mdccccli
            Values for GODLESS and GOTHIC florins on page 66

ELIZABETH II   *Decimal Patterns*

1 CENT - 1961 - ER - ONE DECIMAL PENNY - Bronze 20mm
2 CENTS - crown, ornamented trident - 1961 - Bronze 25mm
(1986 set of 1961 comprising 1, 2, 5, 10, 20 and 50 cents
sold at Sotheby's for £2,400 plus buyers premium and VAT)
Aluminium quarter penny   - Tudor Rose over 1/4 -   20mm
Bronze half penny   -   Welsh Dragon over 1/2 -   17mm
Bronze penny -   Scottish Lion, St Andrews Cross -   20mm
Bronze two pence   -   Britannia over large 2 -   26mm
Cupro-nickel five pence   -   Three Crowns over 5 -   23mm
Cupro-nickel ten pence - St George and The Dragon -   28mm
Cupro-nickel twenty pence - Gartered Royal Arms -   36mm
(in 1982, a decimal pattern for 20p dated 1963   ☯   £1,500)
(in 1986, full set of decimal patterns dated 1963   ☯   £4,500)
(in 1986, uniface set artist's copies at Spink's   ☯   £900)

IN 1982 THE WORD 'NEW' WAS DISCONTINUED

ELIZABETH II

Half New Penny

BRONZE 17mm | THE ROYAL CROWN

Year	Selected	Unc/Proof	Year	Selected	Unc/Proof	Year	Selected	Unc/Proof
1971	1,394,188,250	15p/£2	1977		20p/£1	1982		15p/£1
1972	Proof ex-set	---/£3	1978		25p/£2	1983	7,600,000	25p/£1
1973	365,680,000	50p/£1	1979		20p/£2	1984	158,820	£1/£2
1974	365,448,000	50p/£1	1980		30p/£1			
1975	197,600,000	50p/£1	1981		60p/£1		Demonetized 31/12/84	
1976	256,000,000	50p/£1						

One New Penny

BRONZE 20mm — A PORTCULLIS WITH CHAINS ROYALLY CROWNED

Year	Selected	Unc/Proof	Year	Selected	Unc/Proof	Year	Selected	Unc/Proof
1971	1,521,666,250	15p/£2	1981		60p/£1	1990		10p/£2
1972		---/£1	1982		40p/£1	1991		10p/£2
1973	280,196,000	50p/£1	1983		50p/£1	1992		10p/£2
1974	330,892,000	60p/£1	1984		20p/£1	1993		
1975	221,604,000	60p/£1	1985		20p/£1	1994		
1976	241,800,000	50p/£1	1986		25p/£1	1995		
1977		---/£1	1986		25p/£1			
1978		---/£2	1987		10p/£1			
1979		25p/£2	1988		15p/£1			
1980		25p/£2	1989		10p/£2			

Two New Pence

BRONZE 26mm — THE BADGE OF THE PRINCE OF WALES

Year	Selected	Unc/Proof	Year	Selected	Unc/Proof	Year	Selected	Unc/Proof
1971	1,454,856,250	15p/£1	1981		30p/£1.5	1988		20p/£1.5
1972, 1973, 1974		---/£3	1982		£2/£4	1989		20p/£1
1975	144,406,000	75p/£1	1983		£2/£4	1990		15p/£2
1976	135,772,000	75p/£1	1983 ★ with old rev.			1991		15p/£2
1977		25p/£1	1984		£1/£2	1992		15p/£2
1978		£1/£2	1985		20p/£1	1993		
1979	408,527,000	30p/£2	1986		20p/£1	1994		
1980		25p/£1	1987		20p/£1.5	1995		

1983 ★ two authenticated examples, so far, still inscribed 'NEW'.
1985 New MAKLOUF PORTRAIT of The Queen (see page 42)

FIVE PENCE

CUPRO-NICKEL 23mm	Selected	Unc/Proof		Selected	Unc/Proof
1968	98,868,250	50p/--	1981		---/£2
1969	119,270,000	75p/--	1982		£2/£4
1970	225,948,525	75p/--	1983		£1/£2
1971	81,783,475	75p/£2	1984		£1/£2
1972, 1973, 1974		---/£2	1985		£1/£2
1975	86,550,000	50p/£2	1986		£1/£2
1976		---/£2	1987		50p/£2
1977		35p/£2	1988		50p/£2
1978	61,000,000	£4/£5	1989		40p/£2
1979		40p/£3	1990		£2/£3
1980		30p/£2			

A THISTLE ROYALLY CROWNED

	Selected	Unc/Proof
SMALLER 18mm COIN		20p/£2
1990	35,000 silver pairs of both sizes £24.50	
1990	20,000 silver Piedfort £28.95	20p/£2
1991		20p/£2
1992		20p/£2
1993		
1994		
1995		

TEN PENCE

CUPRO-NICKEL 28.5mm	Selected	Unc/Proof		Selected	Unc/Proof
1968	336,143,250	60p/--	1978		---/£3
1969	314,008,000	60p/--	1979		£1/£3
1970	133,571,000	£2/--	1980		£1/£3
1971	63,205,000	£2/£3	1981		£1/£3
1972		---/£5	1982		£3/£5
1973	152,174,000	£1/£3	1983		£1/£3
1974	92,741,000	£2/£4	1984		£1/£3
1975	181,559,000	£1/£3	1985		£1/£3
1976	196,745,000	£1/£3	1986		£1/£3
1977		£1/£3	1987		£2/£3

A LION PASSANT GUARDANT ROYALLY CROWNED

	Selected	Unc/Proof
1988		£2/£3
1989		£2/£3
1990		£2/£5
1991		£3/£5
1992		50p/£2
SMALLER 24.5mm		50p/£2
1993		----

The florin/two shilling/tenpence piece was demonetized 30/6/93.

TWENTY PENCE

CUPRO-NICKEL 21.4mm	Selected	Unc/Proof		Selected	Unc/Proof
1982	740,815,000	50p/£6	1989	109,128,890	45p/£4
1982	25,000 silver Piedfort	--/£34	1990		50p/£5
1983	158,463,000	50p/£5	1991		50p/£5
1984	65,350,965	75p/£5	1992		....
1985	75,273,699	50p/£5	1993		....
1986		£1/£5	1994		....
1987	137,450,000	75p/£5			
1988	38,038,344	45p/£4			

A DOUBLE ROSE ROYALLY CROWNED

TWENTYFIVE PENCE 38mm

CUPRO - NICKEL CURRENCY :			.925 SILVER PROOF :		
		Selected Unc.		F.D.C. from / to	
1972	7,452,100 Silver Wedding	65p	100,000	£12/£18	
1972	Cupro nickel proofs from sets £3/£4				
1977	36,989,000 Silver Jubilee 55p/60p		377,000	£9/£12	
1977	Cupro nickel proofs from sets £3/£4				
1977	Selected coin in R.M. folder £1/£2				
1980	Queen Mother's 80th Birthday:				
	9,477,513	50p/60p	83,672	£20/£30	
1980	Selected coin in R.M. folder 50p/£1				
1981	27,360,279 Royal Wedding £1		218,142	£15/£25	
1981	Selected coin in R.M. folder 50p/£1				

1989   FOUR-CROWN-COLLECTION of the four silver proofs   £125
(The Case, Booklet and Certificate are, probably, vital to the valuation of this group of coins : see individual values).

FIFTY PENCE
CUPRO-NICKEL 30 mm

Date	Selected Unc/Proof		Date	Sel.Unc/Proof	Date	Sel.Unc/Proof
1969	188,400,000	£2/£4	1980	£2/£4	1988	£3/£5
1970	19,461,000	£2/£4	1981	£2/£4	1989	£3/£5
1973 ★	89,775,000	£2/£4	1982	£2/£5	1990	£3/£6
★	356,616 proofs	£4	1983	£2/£5	1991	£3/£6
1976	28,100,000	£2/£4	1984	£2/£5	1992	/£5
1977		£2/£4	1985	£2/£5	1992/93 ★★	/£5
1978		£2/£4	1986	£2/£5	★★ Silver	£24
1979		£2/£4	1987	£2/£5	★★ Piedfort	£45

★ EEC Commemoratives ★★ Gold £375

★★ New design to commemmorate Britain's Presidency/Council of Ministers

ONE POUND (One Hundred Pence)

Pale-yellow mixture of metals - 22.5 mm dia. - 3.1 mm thick
has grained (milled) edge, with incuse (struck in) lettering.
England and Northern Ireland variants read: DECUS ET TUTAMEN
(An Ornament and a Safeguard) first used to prevent the "clipping" of coins

Scotland: NEMO ME IMPUNE LACESSIT (No One Provokes Me with Impunity)
For Wales: PLEIDOL WYF I'M GWALD (True Am I to My Country)

Date	Mintage		Unc./Proof
1983	434,000,000	Royal Coat of Arms general issue	£2/£3
1983	484,900	Selected general issue in wallet	£3
1983	50,000	Sterling silver (.925) proofs	£20
1983	10,000	Silver Piedfort proofs.	£110
1984	110,000,000	Thistle for Scotland general issue	£1/£2
1984	27,960	Selected general issue in wallet	£3
1984	44,855	Sterling silver (.925) proofs	£22
1984	15,000	Silver Piedfort proofs.	£50
1985	178,000,000	Leek for Wales general issue	£1
1985		Selected general issue in wallet	£2.60
1985	50,000	Sterling silver (.925) proofs	£22
1985	15,000	Silver Piedfort proofs.	£50

One Pound   continued from previous page   ★ ISSUE PRICE
Unc / Proof

1986	Not revealed	Flax Plant for Northern Ireland	£1/£3
		Selected general issue in wallet	£2.60
1986	50,000	Sterling silver (.925) proofs	£19.95
1986	15,000	Silver Piedfort proofs.	£38.50
1987		An Oak Tree for general issue	£1/£3
		Selected general issue in wallet	£2.75
1987	50,000	Sterling silver (.925) proofs	£19.95
1987	15,000	Silver Piedfort proofs.	£38.50
1988		The Royal Arms of H.M. The Queen (Derek Gorringe)	£1/£3
		Selected general issue in wallet	£2.75
1988	50,000	Sterling silver (.925) proofs	£19.95
1988	15,000	Silver Piedfort proofs.	£39.50
1989		Re-appearance of the Thistle Pound	£1/£3
1989	25,000	Sterling silver (.925) proofs	£19.95
1989	10,000	Silver Piedfort proofs.	£39.50
1990		Re-appearance of the Leek Pound	£1/£3
1990	25,000	Sterling silver (.925) proofs	£21.25
1991		Re-appearance of the Flax Pound	£1/£3
1991	25,000	Sterling silver (.925) proofs	£22.50
1992		General Issue (Oak Tree)	£1/£3
1992	25,000	Sterling silver (.925) proofs	£23.50
1993		General Issue · Royal Arms	£1/£3
1993	25,000	Sterling silver (.925) proofs	£23.50
1993	12,500	Silver Peidfort proofs	£44.50
1994		General Issue	- - - -
1994		Sterling silver (.925) proofs	- - - -

★ Proofs for all years appear following removal from the
  sets; these are offered at £2 to £3 : not issue prices.

1986 COMMEMORATING EDINBURGH COMMONWEALTH GAMES

Thistle, Wreath, Cross of St.Andrew	£2		Selected in wallet		£4
125,000	Nickel-brass proofs in sets	--		125,000 .500 silver	£14
75,000	925 silver proofs	£25		15,000 gold proofs	£280

1989 COMMEMORATING 300th ANNIVERSARY BILL OF RIGHTS

William & Mary. Not for general issue, but still legal tender.

	Bill of Rights	£2	Selected in wallet	£3.95
	Claim of Right	£2	Selected in wallet	£3.95
	Pair, as picture, loose, but of selected quality			£6.50
	Pair, as picture, selected, in Official blister-pack			£7.25
25,000 each	Bill and Claim proofs in silver singles			£22.50

Included above: Bill AND Claim proofs in silver sold as a pair £42.50
Noted (1991) (F. J. Jeffrey & Son Ltd.) £44.00 inc. postage

10,000 pairs   Bill AND Claim proofs, silver, piedfort, pairs   £77.50

FIVE POUNDS ('Crown')

1990 COMMEMORATING THE QUEEN MOTHER's 90th BIRTHDAY

Interlaced Es - Rose and Thistle - Legal Tender £5

	Selected cupro-nickel in official blister-pack Issued ●		£8.95
150,000	Proofs in Sterling Silver	Issued ●	£28.75
2,500	Proofs in 22 carat Gold	Issued ●	£625.00

1993   THE CORONATION ANNIVERSARY 1953/1993

Queen's 1953 portrait encircled by mounted trumpeters/swords/sceptres

	Selected cupro-nickel in official blister-pack Issued ●		£8.95
100,000	Proofs in Sterling Silver	Issued ●	£29.50
2,500	Proofs in 22 carat Gold	Issued ●	£625.00

F. D. C.
from / to

GEORGE IV

| 1826 | 140 sets | (11) Farthing to five pounds | £17,000/£20,000 |

WILLIAM IV

| 1831 | 145 sets | (14) Maundy replaces £5 | £12,500/£18,000 |
| | Silver only | (8) (Spink 1988) E.F. £4,400 | - - - - - - |

VICTORIA

1839	300 sets	(15) In spade shaped case which includes:	
		the Una-and-The-Lion gold £5	£21,000/£25,000
1853	460 (16)	Quarter-farthing to Gothic 5/-	£14,500/£18,500
1887	797 sets	(11) unofficial cases 3d to £5	£3,750/£5,750
1887	287 sets	3d to 5/-	£800/£1,000
1893	773 sets	(10) rarely intact 3d to £5	£4,000/£6,000
1893	Short set of six silver coins	3d to 5/-	£800/£1,000

EDWARD VII

| 1902 | 8,066 sets | (13) Maundy 1d to £5 (matt) | £1,400/£1,800 |
| 1902 | 7,057 sets | (11) Maundy 1d to sovereign | £350/£500 |

GEORGE V

1911	2,812 sets	(12) Maundy 1d to £5	£2,000/£2,500
1911	952 sets	(10) Maundy 1d to sovereign	£600/£750
1911	2,241 sets	(8) Maundy penny to half-crown	£200/£325
1927	15,030 sets	(6) 3d to crown	£185/£250

GEORGE VI

1937	5,501 sets	(4) Half-sovereign to £5	£1,200/£1,500
1937	26,402 sets	(15) Farthing to crown + Maundy	£90/£120
1950	17,513 sets	(9) Farthing to half-crown	£30/£45
1951	20,000 sets	(10) Farthing to crown	£40/£55

ELIZABETH II

1953	40,000 sets	(10) Farthing to crown (5/-)	£30/£42
1953	★ A large number of sets in plastic wallet (9)		£8/£9.50
1968	★ Decimal souvenir sets, mixed dates in folder		£1
1970	750,000	Last Sterling $1/2$ d to 2/6d + medallion	£8/£12

★ non-proof, selected currency coins

* = plus Royal Mint medallion

				F.D.C. from/to
1971	350,000	(6)	half to 50p	£10/£12
1972	150,000	(7) ★	plus Crown	£10/£12
1973	100,000	(6) ★	half to EEC 50p	£7/£9
1974	100,000	(6) ★	half to 50p	£6/£8
1975	100,000	(6) ★	half to 50p	£7/£9
1976	100,000	(6) ★	half to 50p	£7/£9
1977	193,000	(7) ★	Jubilee Crown	£10/£14
1978	88,100	(6) ★	half to 50p	£12/£16
1979	81,000	(6) ★	half to 50p	£12/£18
1980	10,000	(4)	half-sov to £5	£900
1980	143,400	(6) ★	half to 50p	£5/£10
1981	5,000	(9)	½p to gold £5	£600
1981	2,500	(2)	crown & sov.	£90/£140
1981	100,300	(6) ★	half to 50p	£5/£10
1982	2,500	(4)	half-sov to £5	£1,050
1982	106,800	(7) ★	plus new 20p	£5/£10
1982	205,000	(7)	Uncirc in folder	£3/£5
1983	12,500	(3)	½ sov, sov, £2	£350
1983	107,800	(6) ★	plus 20p & £1	£8/£14
1983	637,100	(8)	Uncirc in folder	£5/£6
1984	7,095	(3)	½ sov, sov, £5	£750
1984	125,000	(8) ★	Scottish £1	£8/£14
1984	158,820	(8)	Uncirc in folder	£5/£6

1985	125,000	(7) ★	1p to Welsh £1 Maklouf	
			portrait, blue leatherette case	£18.75
			de-luxe red leather case	£25.75
1985		(7)	Uncirc in folder	£4.75
1986	125,000	(8) ★	N.I. £1 & C/wealth £2,	
			in blue leatherette case	£21.25
			in de-luxe red leather case	£28.25
1986		(8)	Uncirc in folder	£7.95
1987	125,000	(7) ★	1p to English Oak £1	
			in blue leatherette case	£18.95
			in de-luxe red leather case	£25.95
1987		(7)	Uncirc in folder	£5.25
1988	125,000	(7) ★	1p to Royal Arms £1	
			in blue leatherette case	£18.95
			in de-luxe red leather case	£25.95
1988		(7)	Uncirc in folder	£5.25
1989	125,000	(8) ★	1p to 'Orange' £2 x 2	
			in blue leatherette case	£22.95
			in de-luxe red leather case	£29.95
1989		(8)	Uncirc in folder	£5.75
1989			Boy/Girl Baby Packs in Blue/Pink	
			either @	£9.95

* = plus Royal Mint medallion

1990	100,000	(8) ★	1p, (both 5p),	
			50p to Welsh £1 :	
			in blue leatherette case	£21.95
			in de-luxe red leather case	£28.95
1990		(8)	Uncirc in folder	£6.25
1990			Boy/Girl Baby Packs in Blue/Pink	
			either @	£9.95
1991	100,000	(7) ★	1p,to N.I. £1	
			in blue leatherette case	£23.50
			in de-luxe red leather case	£30.60
1991		(8)	Uncirc in folder	£7.10
1991			Baby Packs	£11.20
1991			L.s.d. set (dated 1967)	£14.25
1992	100,000	(9) ★	1p, (10p x 2), (50p x 2) to £1	
			in blue leatherette case	£27.50
			in de-luxe red leather case	£34.50
1992		(9)	uncirc in folder	£8.75
1992			Baby Packs	£13.95
1992			Wedding Pack	£13.95
1993	100,000	(8) ★	1p to £5	
			in blue leatherette case	£28.75
			in de-luxe red leather case	£35.50
1993		(8)	uncirc 1p to £1 (50p x 2)	£8.75
1993			Baby Gift Set	£13.95
1993			Wedding Collection	£16.50
1994	100,000	( ) ★	1p to £1	
1994			in blue leatherette case	......
			in de-luxe red leather case	......
1994		( )	uncirc in folder	......
1994			Baby Gift Set	......
1994			Wedding Collection	......
1995	100,000	( ) ★	1p to £1	
1995			in blue leatherette case	......
			in de-luxe red leather case	......
1995		( )	uncirc in folder	......
1995			Baby Gift Set	......
1995			Wedding Collection	......